Poetry and Prose of the Han, Wei and Six Dynasties

Panda Books

First Edition 2005

ISBN 7-119-03356-5

© Foreign Languages Press, Beijing, China, 2005

Published by Foreign Languages Press

24 Baiwanzhuang Road, Beijing 100037, China

Website: http://www.flp.com.cn

E-mail Address: info@flp.com.cn

sales@flp.com.cn

Distributed by China International Book Trading Corporation

35 Chegongzhuang Xilu, Beijing 100044, China

P.O. Box 399, Beijing, China

Printed in the People's Republic of China

CONTENTS

CONTENTS

Publisher's Note

THIS book is a selection of poetry and prose written between the beginning of the Han Dynasty in 206 BC and the reunification of China under the Sui Dynasty in AD 589. The Han fell in AD 220, and its empire split into the Three Kingdoms of Wei in the north, Shu in the west and Wu in the south. These were reunited in AD 265 by the Jin Dynasty, which was in AD 317 forced to abandon the north to barbarian incursions. The north collapsed into a welter of feuding regimes punctuated only by the relatively unified Northern Wei Dynasty (AD 386-534). The south, however, remained fairly stable, the Jin being succeeded by the Song, Qi, Liang and Chen Dynasties until the last of these fell to the Sui, whose predecessor the Northern Zhou had united the north in AD 577.

As will be seen from the body of the book, the events of the fourth century shifted the cultural axis of China from the valley of the Yellow River south to that of the Yangtse.

The *fu* or verse essay popular in the first half of the Han Dynasty had its origins in the preceding Warring States period (475-221 BC), particularly in the southern kingdom of Chu, and was used principally as a vehicle of political statement, frequently of indignation by statesmen whose advice had been repudiated. *The Owl* by Jia Yi is a good example of this unyielding spirit and refusal to associate with unscrupulous men.

The *yuefu* style took its name from the Music Bureau set up in the reign of the Han Emperor Wu (140-87 BC) to compose music, train musicians and collect songs and became synonymous with the folk-song style of the period. The *yuefu* corpus contains many narrative ballads, one of the best being *The Bride of Jiao Zhongqing*, a long work telling how the feudal ethics of the patriarchal clan system destroyed the happiness of a young couple, who were able to overcome it only in death.

The later Han was not a time of great literary creation, but the influence of the *yuefu* persisted and is evident in the great number of eminent poets who appeared in the reign of Jian An (AD 196-219), among whom were the warlord Cao Cao (who set up the Wei Dynasty) and his sons Cao Pi and Cao Zhi.

During the Wei and Jin Dynasties most scholars tried to escape reality, and interest in metaphysics was prevalent, as exemplified by such talents as Ruan Ji, Zuo Si and Tao Yuanming.

Tao Yuanming grew up during the late Jin Dynasty, when political influence depended less on virtue and ability than on family connections, social position and wealth. Disgusted by the resultant internecine strife, he retired from official life with its chaos and corruption to a pastoral life of farming and writing. He is the archetype of the "hermit poet".

Tao Yuanming, though much influenced in his poetry by Confucian and Taoist philosophy, may also have written ghost stories. Tales of the supernatural had become popular since the fall of the Han and continued in vogue down to the end of the Southern Dynasties. This may be partly ascribed to the growing influence of Buddhism, introduced into China during the Han. The same period saw much translation of Buddhist works, as well as the appearance of Fa Xian's *Record of Buddhist Countries*. Be that as it may, the supernatural element joined with the traditional folk legend to reflect the loves and hatreds of the people and denounce social inequality in its more preposterous manifestations, especially the licence and cruelty of the ruling class.

Such idle reflection on the conduct of others was encouraged by the political circumstances of the Wei and Jin Dynasties, and is reflected not only in folk literature. The stories from Liu Yiqing's *New Anecdotes of Social Talk* illustrate the scholarly and courtly aspects of this trend.

The last section of our book is devoted to the literary treatise *Carving a Dragon at the Core of Literature* by Liu Xie, whose life extended over the Song, Qi and Liang Dynasties of the south.

Despite the prevalence of chaos during this long period and the high-handed policies which plagued the life of the intellect, there appeared a great number of outstanding writers and significant works. We have been at great pains to cull from the diversity of the period some pieces which will give the reader an intimation of its wonder and its delight.

Han-Dynasty Verse Essays

THE author of *The Owl*, Jia Yi (201-169 BC), was born in Luo-yang in Henan Province during the Western Han Dynasty. Already well-known as a literary talent by the age of 18, he was summoned to court by the Emperor Wen and made a minister for his proposals on political reform and the weakening of the powers of the nobility. Court slander brought about his removal from the centre of power, and he was relegated to the post of tutor to a prince in the south. There, at Changsha, he wrote *The Owl* as a lament for his failure and died of grief at the age of 32.

The Owl

In the year Chan E, [*]
The fourth month in early summer,
On the Geng Zi day at sunset
An owl came to my house and stopped by my seat,
Looking thoroughly at ease.
Amazed by this strange apparition,
I opened the book of oracles
To learn what this portended,
And there I read:
"A wild bird's entry into a house
Foretells the master's departure."
I asked the owl then:
"Where am I to go?
Tell me, pray, if good fortune awaits me
Or some calamity, if I am ill-fated.
Will it come soon or late?
Let me know the date!"
Sighing, the owl raised its head and flapped its wings.
As it could not speak, I could only guess its meaning:
All creation changes, nothing is at rest;
Ceaseless the flux — progression and retrogression —
Matter becoming immaterial in endless transformations,
Their infinite subtlety defying description!
In calamity lies good fortune
And in good fortune lurks calamity,

---

[*] 174 BC.

Grief and joy knocking together at the door,

Good luck and ill inhabiting the same realm.

Wu was powerful yet Fu Chai lost the kingdom;

The Yues fled to Kuaiji yet Gou Jian ruled supreme; [*]

Li Si's travels were crowned with success,

Yet he was tortured to death. [**]

Fu Yue, a shackled slave,

Became Wu Ding's chief minister. [***]

Thus good fortune and bad are interlaced;

Fate is unpredictable,

And none knows what the end will be.

Water forced will spurt out,

An arrow drawn taut will fly far;

Nature is a ceaseless cycle

With everything transmuted, interacting.

Clouds gather and rain falls;

Endless the universal evolution;

None can fathom Heaven or make plans for the future.

Who knows how soon or late he must meet his fate?

The universe is a furnace stoked by Nature,

With the *yin* and *yang* [****] as fuel,

The myriad things as metal;

---

[*] Fu Chai (?-473 BC), the king of Wu, first defeated the Kingdom of Yue but later was conquered by the king of Yue, Gou Jian.

[**] Li Si (?-208 BC), a statesman of Qin, helped Qin Shi Huang to subdue other states and unify China. After Qin Shi Huang's death, his rival Zhao Gao had Li Si torn limb from limb.

[***] According to a legend, Fu Yue was a slave before becoming a high official in the Shang Dynasty (16th-11th century BC).

[****] The dual principles — female and male, negative and positive — of ancient Chinese philosophy.

Gathering, scattering and vanishing,
Nothing is ever constant;
Countless the permutations
Continuing without end.
If one chances to be born a man,
Why cling to life?
And why feel dismay
If reborn in a different form?
Small minds take a selfish view,
Regarding all else but themselves as worthless;
Men of understanding take a broader view,
Not caring into what form they may turn.
The greedy will die for wealth, the gallant for fame,
And the ambitious for power;
But the vulgar value their lives.
Those under stress may race now east, now west,
But a great man will not bend
And remains constant through vicissitudes.
A hidebound pedant is fettered by tradition,
But a pure man spurns all things
And clings to the Truth alone.
The confused multitude are biassed
With a million prejudices;
A true man is tranquil
And rests alone with the Truth,
Renouncing intellect and spurning material things,
Remaining aloof and unconcerned for himself,
He roams at will in the infinite with the Truth.
He will flow with the current,

Stop when he reaches a bank,
And abandon himself to fate with no thought of self.
His life is like drifting
And his death like resting,
Tranquil as a calm, deep pool,
Untrammelled as a boat adrift;
For instead of prizing his life
He floats in a void.
The truly good man has no impediments
But accepts his fate undismayed.
As nothing matters a straw,
Why should he have misgivings?

Translated by Yang Xianyi
and Gladys Yang

"Yuefu" Folk-Songs

THE *yuefu* was the Music Bureau set up in the second century BC to standardize court music. Apart from ceremonial pieces composed by scholars, it compiled a corpus of folk-songs drawn from all parts of the country for less stately occasions, and it is this popular element which became known as the *yuefu* style, whose freshness and vitality exercised a great influence on the development of formal poetry.

The One I Love

The one I love
Lives south of the great ocean.
What shall I send to greet him?
A tortoise-shell comb with two pearls
Hung from pendants of jade.
They tell me he is untrue
And I shatter the gift and burn it,
Shatter the gift and burn it,
And scatter its ashes to the wind.
From this day on
No more must I think of him,
No more must I think of the time
When the crowing of a cock, the barking of a dog,
Made me tremble lest my brother and his wife hear us.
Shrill wails the autumn wind,
Swift the sparrow-hawk takes flight;
Soon the sun will rise in the east
And shed light upon my heart!

A Pledge

By heaven,
I shall love you
To the end of time!
Till mountains crumble,

Streams run dry,

Thunder rumbles in winter,

Snow falls in summer,

And the earth mingles with the sky —

Not till then will I cease to love you!

Gathering Lotus

South of the river is the place to gather lotus,

 Where among teeming leaves

 Fish dart and play!

 North and south,

 East and west,

Between the lotus leaves they dart and play!

A Crow's Fate

A crow with fledglings eight or nine

Nested on a cassia tree in the Qins' yard —

      Caw!

The son of the family was a reckless youth,

An adept with a powerful catapult

And pellets mixed with balsam.

A catapult and two pellets in his left hand,

He circled about the birds —

      Caw!

His first pellet dealt our crow a mortal wound
And straight to heaven above her spirit soared!

This mother bird laid her eggs
Among the boulders of the South Hill —
                                                  Caw!
Her fledglings were safely hidden away from men,
For the twisting path through the hills was hard to find.
Ah, but white deer in the emperor's park at Shanglin
Are bagged by archers for dried venison;
Wild swan which fly to the vault of the sky
Are captured and cooked for the palace;
And the carp in the depths of the River Luo
May find a hook in its mouth —
                                                  Caw!
All men have their allotted span of life,
Then why complain whether death comes soon or late?

The Eastern Gate

Outside the eastern gate
He hardly dare go home;
Once over the threshold,
He chokes with grief again.

Not a peck of rice left in the pot,
Not a coat on the peg behind...

Sword in hand he starts back to the eastern gate,
But his wife clutches at his sleeve and weeps.

"Others may hanker after rank and riches,
I am content to share your gruel with you.
By the blue sky above,
Think of your unweaned child!
Do not do this thing!"

"Bah! Let me go!
Already it is too late.
Are we to drag on like this
Till our hair is white?"

A Wife Longs for Her Husband

Green, green, the grass by the river,
And in thought I follow it far, far away;
So far that I can hardly picture him,
And yet last night I saw him in a dream;
In a dream he was by my side,
But I woke and he was in a distant land,
A distant land, strange parts;
Tossing and turning I longed for him in vain.
Even a withered mulberry feels the wind,
Even the ocean water feels the cold.

Men come home to fondle their dear ones.

Who would carry word to me?

But a stranger from far away

Brings me two fine carp. *

I call the boy to cook them

And find in them a message on white silk.

I kneel to read —

What does his letter say?

"Take good care of your health," he starts,

And ends, "You are every moment in my thoughts."

Homesick

Flitting, flitting, the swallows before the hall;

In winter they vanish, in summer they return;

Yet I, with two brothers of my own,

Am still a wanderer in a strange land.

Who will patch my old clothes?

Who will stitch and mend for me?

The good woman of the house is kind.

She takes my clothes and mends them;

But her husband coming home,

Framed in the doorway, looks askance at me.

I tell him, "No call to look at me like that!

When a brook is clear the stones are seen."

---

* In ancient times letters were placed between two pieces of wood cut in the shape of a fish.

My conscience is crystal clear.
Just let me end my wanderings and go home!

To a Faithless Husband

Plain as snow on the hills,
Clear as moon among the clouds
Is your change of heart, they tell me;
And so I've come to bid you good-bye.
Today we've drunk a measure of wine;
Tomorrow we must part by the canal.
I shall walk beside the royal canal,
Whose waters flow east and are gone,
And wonder if my grief will ever end.
No girl need cry when she's married
If her husband is a single-hearted man
Who will not leave her till her hair is white.
Pliant the bamboo fishing rod, *
Wet, wet, the tail of the fish.
A man who valued constancy
Would set no store by money!

---

* In old Chinese folk-songs "fishing" was often a covert allusion to lovers' meeting. The neglected wife is thinking back to their courtship.

The Fan

Fine, freshly woven silk of Qi
Is white as frost or snow;
A piece, embroidered, makes a fan
As round as the bright moon.
My lord keeps the fan about him.
Its motion makes a gentle breeze for him;
But I dread the coming of autumn,
When cold winds steal away the sultry heat
And the fan is tossed, unwanted, into a casket,
Its short term of favour ended.

A Butterfly Caught by a Swallow

A butterfly, flitting through the eastern garden,
I am caught among the clover
By a swallow foraging for her young in spring!
She carries me off deep into the purple palace
And wheels around the capital of a pillar;
Her fledglings hop for joy
At sight of the food in her beak,
Craning their necks and eagerly flapping their wings.

Far from Home

I sing a song of grief instead of weeping,
Stare into the distance instead of going home,
And dream of my native village,
My heart full to bursting.
I would go back but have no one to help me;
I would cross the river but there is no boat.
No words can tell my longing.
It seems as if wheels were grinding over my heart!

The Dried Fish

The dried fish, ferried across the river, weeps;
Too late he repents his folly!
He writes a letter to the bream and tench,
Warning them to be more wary!

To a Husband Far Away

Soft and pliant, the lonely bamboo
Rooted in the mountain;
But, married to you,
I am like the dodder clinging to a vine.

As the dodder has its season of growth,
So husband and wife should have time to be together,
Yet a thousand *li* divide us since we married,
Far-stretching mountain ranges lie between.
Longing for you makes me old before my time,
It seems your covered carriage will never come!
I grieve for the orchid,
So splendid when it flowers,
For unless plucked in time
It will only wither away like the grass in autumn.
What can I do
But trust to your constancy?

Parted Lovers

Far, far away, the Cowherd,
Fair, fair, the Weaving Maid; *
Nimbly move her slender white fingers,
Click-clack goes her spinning-loom.
All day she weaves, yet her web is still not done
And her tears fall like rain.
Clear and shallow the Milky Way,
They are not far apart!
But the stream brims always between
And, gazing at each other, they cannot speak.

---

* The Cowherd and the Weaving Maid are the Chinese names for constellations separated by the Milky Way.

The Old Wife and the New

She went up the hill to pluck nettle-seed,
She came down the hill and met her former husband.
She knelt and asked her former husband:
"How do you find your new wife?"

"My new wife is good,
But no match for the old one.
In looks there is little to choose,
But she is less clever with her hands."
"Your new wife came in through the front door,
Your old wife left by the side door."

"My new wife is good at weaving raw silk,
My old wife at weaving white silk;
One weaves forty feet of raw silk a day,
The other fifty feet and more of white silk.
If you compare raw silk and white,
The new wife is not up to the old."

Translated by Yang Xianyi
and Gladys Yang

A Song in Slow Time

Green the mallow in the garden,
Waiting for sunlight to dry the morning dew;
Bright spring diffuses virtue,
Adding fresh lustre to all living things.
Yet I dread the coming of autumn
When leaves turn yellow and the flowers fade.
A hundred streams flow eastwards to the ocean,
Nevermore to turn west again;
And one who misspends his youth
In old age will grieve in vain.

East of Pingling *

East of Pingling,
Pines, cedars and plane trees.
Who has carried off our good man?
Carried him off to the high hall
And demanded from him one million cash and two horses.
Two horses — that is certainly hard!
His heart sinks at sight of the officers pressing him.
His heart sinks, his blood runs cold.
"I must go home and tell them to sell the young bullock."

---

* Pingling, near present-day Xi'an, was the burial place of Emperor Zhao Di, who reigned from 86-74 BC.

Fighting South of the City

There is fighting south of the city,
Slaughter on the northern outskirts;
The dead lie unburied in the wilds,
Serving as carrion for crows.
Beg the crows for me:
"Lament these strangers first!
Dead in the wilds, not likely to be buried,
How can their carrion escape you?"
Deep and clear the water, dark the reeds:
Brave horsemen fought here and died;
Their jaded steeds linger on, neighing.
If houses are built on the bridge,
Who can cross to north or south?
If crops are left unharvested,
What food will there be for our lord?
And his would-be subjects —
How can they remain loyal?
Take thought indeed for them,
These loyal subjects are worthy of remembrance;
They went out in the morning to fight,
But in the evening did not return.

Captain of the Guard

The Huo family had a slave,
Feng Zidu by name;
Relying on the power of the High Marshal,
He ogled a Hunnish maid serving in a tavern.
This girl just turned fifteen
Was alone in the tavern one spring day
In a long gown with double girdle,
Wide sleeves and a jacket with mimosa design.
In her hair she wore jade from Lantian;
Behind her ears, pearls from Byzantium;
And so charming her two tresses,
Their like could nowhere be found,
For one tress alone was worth five million cash,
The two of them more than ten.
Who would have thought this young captain of the guard,
So debonair, would drop in!
Dazzling his silver saddle,
His carriage with kingfisher canopy waiting outside,
He asked me for clear wine,
And I raised the jade wine-pot by its silken cord;
Then he asked for a tasty dish,
And I gave him sliced carp on a golden plate.
Presenting me with a bronze mirror,
He tried to fasten it to my red silk gown;
But I would rather have my red silk torn
Than let anybody touch my worthless body!

A man will always love a second woman,
But a girl must respect her husband;
And though one has old friends and new in life,
High and low should never mix.
So thank you, captain of the guard,
Your love for me is quite worthless!

The Ailing Wife

A wife, ill for many years,
Calls her husband to her;
Unable at first to speak,
Tears course down her cheeks.
"Take good care, sir, of our children;
Don't let them go hungry or cold,
And if they do wrong don't beat them with a bamboo,
Or their lives will be cut short —
Remember!"

Envoi

I want to carry the child but he has no gown;
His short jacket is unpadded.
I close the door and window
To go to market, leaving him behind.

On the way I meet a friend
And sit weeping, unable to rise,
Begging him to buy my motherless child a cake,
Speaking to him I cannot stop my tears.
"How can I get the better of my grief?"
I take money from my pocket for my friend.
Home again, I see my little son
Crying for his mother to hold him,
Toddling in the empty room.
"He will come to this too in the end.
Better leave him and forget him!"

By the Roadside Mulberry

The morning sunlight
Shines on the Qin mansion
Whose pride is the lady,
The lady Luofu.
For the silkworms she tendeth
She strippeth the mulberries
Which grow to the south;
From the cassia her basket
Hangs by a silk ribbon;
She has hair neatly braided,
Pearl ear-rings like moon-beams,
Silk petticoat yellow
And apron of purple.

When a wayfarer sees her
He sets down his burden
Awhile, strokes his beard.
A youth when he sees her
Doffs cap and salutes.
The ploughman leaves ploughing,
The hoer his hoeing,
And back in their houses
Find fault with their wives,
Having gazed on Luofu.

From the south comes a lordling
In carriage and five;
Surprised, halts and sends one
To make an inquiry,
"Who is that beauty,
And who are her kin?"
"She is one of the Qins,
And her name is Luofu."
"And what may her age be?"
"Her summers not twenty,
Yet more than fifteen."
Then he, condescending,
Says, "Luofu, will't please you
To enter my carriage?"
She faces him boldly,
And thus makes reply:

."What nonsense you talk, sir!

You have your own wife,
And I my own husband.
From the east ride a thousand
With him at their head.
And how shall you know him?
By the white horse he rides,
By the black colt that follows,
Their silk-braided tails
And their gold-braided halters;
By the sword at his side,
With its hilt of jade fashioned,
For which he paid millions.
At the age of fifteen
He kept prefecture minutes,
A scribe in his twenties,
At thirty a minister;
Now, being forty,
He governs a district.
His skin is so fair
And he wears a long beard.
He moves in the yamen
With step slow and stately;
He sits among thousands
Who own him their best."

Song of the Orphan

The orphan's lot
From his hapless birth
Is sorrow unending.
My parents living,
I rode in style,
Four horses to draw me.
My parents dead,
My own brother bid me —
And so did his wife —
Fare forth as a pedlar.
To Jiujiang southward,
To Qi and Lu eastward...
In the twelfth moon returned
But my woes dared not voice.
Lice in my hair,
My skin grimed with dust.
My brother said: Cook for us!
'His wife: Tend the beasts!
In and out of the hall
I fetched and I carried...
No wonder, poor orphan,
My tears flowed like rain.
At dawn fetching water,
Not finished till dark;
Hands chapped and bleeding,
Feet all unshod

On the cruel hoarfrost.
Thorns by the thousand
I plucked out: the smart
Remained in my flesh...
All anguish was I,
And salt tears welled forth,
Pearl after pearl.
Winter, no warm coat,
Summer, no shirt.
A joyless life!
Better follow the dead
To the underworld!
The spring awakened
And all grew green.
The third moon brought silkworms,
The sixth, came the gourds.
With a cartload of melons
I was homeward bound,
When over it went.
How few came to help me,
But how many ate!
They might leave the stalks
For my tyrants to see!
Now I hasten back,
Thinking hard what to do...
In conclusion: What turmoil
Around, and for what?
I'd fain send a letter:
Dear, dead parents, oh!

I can bear it no longer,
I'll join you below!

Translated by Eric Edney
and Yu Baoqu

Poems of the Wei, Jin and Later Periods

THE poets selected are Cao Cao, Cao Zhi, Ruan Ji, Zuo Si, Xie Lingyun and Xie Tiao.

Cao Cao (AD 155-220) was born at Qiao in the principality of Pei, now Boxian in Anhui, and culminated his career as a warlord by setting up the Wei Dynasty of the Three Kingdoms. Personally ruthless by reputation — his name is used in the Chinese equivalent of "talk of the devil" — he nonetheless shows in his poetry considerable sympathy for the sufferings of the common people.

Cao Zhi (AD 192-232) was Cao Cao's third son, and his writing of essays at the age of ten won him the favour of his father, which he subsequently lost by heavy drinking and vaunting his own talent, to say nothing of his jealousy of his brother Cao Pi, who succeeded their father on the throne. He died a bitter and disappointed man.

Ruan Ji (AD 210-263) was a native of Weishi in present-day Henan Province. Under the dark rule of the Wei Dynasty he lived in seclusion from society and gave himself up to drinking. His poems, though couched in ambiguous terms, are full of metaphor and imbued with the spirit of rebellion.

A writer of the Western Jin Dynasty, Zuo Si (AD 250?-305?) was born at Linzi, now Zibo in Shandong. Of humble origin, he had no opportunity to serve his country except as a secretary. His resentment of the powerful family system found frequent expression in his poetry.

Xie Lingyun (AD 385-433) was born at Yangxia in the principality of Chen, now Taikang in Henan, and lived under the Jin and Song dynasties. He was brought up in luxury and inherited his grandfather's dukedom, though this was later reduced to a marquisate and he was sent to govern Yongjia. Although an official, he devoted much time to travel and is noted for his landscape poetry.

Xie Tiao (AD 464-499) lived under the Song and Qi dynasties. He came from the same clan as Xie Lingyun and is known as Xie the Younger. His poetry is noted for the depiction of nature and for its attention to diction, intonation and antithesis. He rose to be prefect of the principality of Nanhai, was arrested on false charges and died in prison.

Cao Cao

Graveyard Song

East of the Pass gallant knights
Rise in arms to punish traitors; *
First joining forces at Mengjin,
Their goal is Xianyang.**
But their allied armies are at odds;
Irresolute, they straggle like wild geese;
Bent on power and gain they fall out
And are soon at each other's throats.
South of the Huai a young lord takes a royal title,***
And a seal is carved for a monarch in the north;
Men long in arms grow lousy,
Countless those who have lost their lives;
White bones lie bleaching in the wilderness,
For a thousand *li* not a cock is heard to crow.
Of our people only one in a hundred is left —
The thought of this breaks our hearts.

---

* The traitors were the followers of Dong Zhuo.

** Mengjin in present-day Henan was where King Wu of Zhou joined with other local chieftains to attack the last ruler of Shang, traditionally considered a tyrant, in the 11th century BC. Xianyang was the capital of the Qin Dynasty and had been stormed by rebels before the founding of the Han Dynasty. These analogies imply that the aim of their rising against Dong Zhuo was to reunify the country and restore peace.

*** In AD 197 Yuan Shao's cousin Yuan Shu proclaimed himself emperor south of the River Huai. In 191 Yuan Shao tried to set up Liu Yu the govenor of Yuzhou as emperor and had a golden seal made for him.

Gazing Out Across the Ocean

Come east of Jieshi Cliff[*]
I gaze out across the ocean,
Its rolling waves
Studded with rocks and islets;
Dense the trees and bushes here,
Rank the undergrowth;
The autumn wind is soughing,
Huge billows are breaking.
Sun and moon take their course
As if risen from the sea;
The bright galaxy of stars
Seems sprung from the deep.
And so, with joy in my heart,
I hum this song.

Though the Tortoise Lives Long

Though the tortoise blessed with magic powers lives long,
Its days have their allotted span;
Though winged serpents ride high on the mist,
They turn to dust and ashes at the last;
An old war-horse may be stabled,

---

[*] This cliff southwest of Leting County in the province of Hebei has now been submerged by
the sea.

Yet still it longs to gallop a thousand *li*;
And a noble-hearted man though advanced in years
Never abandons his proud aspirations.
Man's span of life, whether long or short,
Depends not on Heaven alone;
One who eats well and keeps cheerful
Can live to a great old age.
And so, with joy in my heart,
I hum this song.

A Song

Wine before us, sing a song.
How long does life last?
It is like the morning dew;
Sad so many days have past.

Sing hey, sing ho!
Deep within my heart I pine.
Nothing can dispel my woe,
Save Du Kang, the god of wine.

Blue, blue the scholar's robe;
Long, long for him I ache.
Preoccupied with you, my lord,
Heavy thoughts for your sake.

To each other cry the deer,
Nibbling grass upon the plain.
When a good friend visits me,
We'll play the lyre once again.

In the sky, the moon is bright;
Yet I can reach it never.
In my heart such sorrow dwells;
Remaining with me ever.

In the fields, our paths crossed;
Your visit was so kind.
Together after our long parting,
Your favours come to mind.

Clear the moon, few the stars;
The crows in southward flight.
Circling three times round the tree,
No branch where to alight.

What if the mountain is high,
Or how deep the sea?
When the Duke of Zhou greeted a guest,
In his service all wished to be.

Cao Zhi

The Fair Maiden

Alluring and shy stands a fair maiden,
Gathering mulberry leaves at the crossroads.
The tender twigs rustle;
The leaves fall one by one.
How white her hands as she bares her arms,
A gold bracelet round her wrist!
On her head a golden sparrow hairpin;
At her waist a green jade pendant,
While encompassing her lovely form,
Pearls, coral and blue glass beads.
In the breeze, her silk blouse flutters
And her light skirt flows.
Glances reveal her shining eyes;
Sighs her breath, orchid sweet.
Travellers en route halt their carriages;
Those resting forget their refreshment.
If someone asks where she lives,
Her home is in the south of the city.
A green, storied house by the highway,
With a high gate and double bars.
Radiant as the morning sun,
Who could not admire her beauty?
Why aren't the matchmakers busy?
Where are the silk and jade betrothal gifts?

This fair maiden longs for a worthy lover;
Yet how hard to find a fitting mate.
In vain people make suggestions,
Ignorant of her ideal.
Wasting her youth away in her home,
At midnight she awakes and sighs.

Ruan Ji

Thoughts

Endless nights;
Then morning again.
I'm wasting away;
My energy drained.
In my chest a burning pain.
There must be changes.
So much to bear;
Yet my wits are insufficient.
I dread lest in a trice
My spirit vanish with the wind.
Always treading on thin ice;
Who knows the fears in my heart?

Zuo Si

Thoughts on History

The bright sun illuminates the clear sky,
Casting a pure light over our sacred land.
Within the purple palace are many mansions,
With soaring canopies like floating clouds.
Behind its imposing gates reside
Princes, barons and the like.
Since the dragon gate I scorn,
Why should I visit this place?
In homespun clothes I leave by the southern gate,
Eagerly striding to follow Xu You's path.
On crags ten thousand feet high I'll shake my gown,
And wash my feet in the river flowing thousands of miles.

Xie Lingyun

Spending the Night at Stone-Gate

At dawn I pluck the orchids in the garden,
Fearing that they wither with the frost.
At dusk I go to rest among the clouds,
Enjoying the moon high above the rocks.
At night birds cry returning to their nests;
Leaves fall when a gust of wind blows.
Many strange sounds assail my ears,
Their echoes reverberating clear and shrill.
Who can share these delights?
Who appreciate my sweet wine?
Since the fair one never comes,
I dry my hair on the southern hill.

Xie Tiao

Ascending Mt Sanshan at Evening
and Gazing at the Capital

Like Wang Can gazing at Chang'an from the bank,
Or Pan Yue at Luoyang, north of the Yellow River,
Here I see in the distance everywhere
Tiled roofs resplendent in the sunlight.
The sky at sunset like a coloured brocade;
The river calm like a skein of white silk.
Crying waterfowl flock to the islet;
Flowers of many hues fill the fragrant meadows.
I wish to return home. Why linger here?
I long to end this merry-making.
When will the time to return come?
Till then my tears like falling rain,
So deeply for home I pine.
Can I help it if my hair turns grey?

Translated by Yang Xianyi
and Gladys Yang

Poems by Tao Yuanming

THE career of Tao Yuanming or Tao Qian (AD 365-427) was divided between the Jin and Song dynasties. He was born at Chaisang in Xunyang, now Jiujiang in Jiangxi, became a minor official at 29 and then resigned to till the land. Unable to support his family, he was persuaded to accept the magistracy of Pengze County. When 80 days later it was suggested he spruce himself up for a visit from his superior he retorted, "I will not bow down to a country boy for five pecks of rice," and immediately left for home, abandoning his post. Even in seclusion he was hounded by misfortune. His house burned down when he was 44, and his last two decades were passed in destitution, though he refused official aid with contempt.

Thinking of the Past in My Cottage at the Beginning of Spring in the Year Gui Mao (AD 403)

The Teacher of old* had a lesson to give to the world:
He cared for his work and not for his poverty.
As I now gaze afar to the endless distance,
I will and resolve ever to work my hardest,
To cleave to my hoe and be content with my calling,
To smile and keep up the hearts of my fellow farmers.
The wind skims far across the level fields,
Where sturdy shoots are sprouting new leaves.
Although I cannot measure my year's produce,
Its present state shows many signs of hope.
There comes a time when I rest from ploughing and plant-
   ing,
But still no Traveller comes to ask me questions!**
When the sun goes down we all go home together;
With soup and with wine I treat my nearest neighbours.
Loudly I sing as I shut my gate of brushwood,
I will remain a man of the fields and furrows!

---

* Confucius.

** Confucius went out of his way in his travels to meet two hermit farmers, Zhang Chu and Jie
   Yi, and ask them questions about their philosophy.

Stopping at Qu E on the Way to My Appointment as Secretary to the General

In my youth I remained aloof from the world of affairs;
Music and books pervaded all my heart.
My clothes were rough, but I was content with myself.
Often my purse was empty, but yet was I happy.
Then came the day when carriages stopped in the lane —
They brought the appointment, the order to dress up and
    go.
For a time I am forced to part from my fields and garden.
My lonely boat sails farther and farther away,
My returning thoughts go winding and winding homewards.
Long, endlessly long, my journey seems,
Uphill and down, three hundred miles and more.
My eyes are tired with unknown roads and rivers,
My mind still full of thoughts of my mountain dwelling.
I look up at the clouds and the birds high-soaring there,
And down at the swimming fish in the water's depth.
Ashamed! For Nature once held sway in my heart.
But who shall say that I shall be bound by my body?
Though now I am forced to do what Fate has destined.
In the end, like the scholar Ban Gu, * I too shall return.

---

* A scholar of the later Han Dynasty who expressed in a poem his longing to dwell in a
hermit's hut.

On Returning to Live in My Own Home in the Country

From youth I was never made for common life;
My nature was ever to love the hills and mountains.
By mischance I fell into the dusty world
And, being gone, stayed there for thirteen years.
A captive bird longs for the woods of old,
The fish in the pond dreams of its native river.
So I have returned to till this southern wild,
To a simple life in my own fields and garden.
Two acres of land surround my home,
My thatched cottage has eight or nine bays,
Willow and elm shade the courtyard,
Peach and plum spread in front of the hall.
Dim, dim in the distance lies the village,
Faintly, faintly you see the smoke of its chimneys.
A dog barks deep in the long lane,
The cock crows on the top of a mulberry tree.
There is no dust and no confusion here,
In these empty rooms, but ample space and to spare.
So long have I lived inside a cage!
Now at last I can turn again to Nature.

Nothing much happens out here in the wild,
Our lonely lane has scarcely seen a carriage.
All the day, our rustic doors are closed,

Quiet rooms keep us from thoughts of the world.
But time and again in the lane that leads to the village,
Parting the grass on our way, we meet with each other;
And when we meet, there's no talk of frivolous matters,
We discuss the progress of our hemp and mulberry.
Every day our seedlings are growing taller,
And every day our lands seem ever broader,
We are often afraid that if frost and sleet should fall
All will be withered away like weeds and grass.

I have planted beans below the southern hill;
The weeds abound — the young bean shoots are few.
Early I rise in the morning to tend my rows,
When I return with my hoe I am wearing the moonlight.
The path is narrow, the flowers and grass are tall,
And my clothes are all drenched in the dews of nightfall.
Wet clothes are little enough to bear,
But let not my purpose be abandoned ever!

The Fire That I Suffered in the Sixth Month of the Year Wushen (AD 408)

For my cottage of reeds and thatch in this poor lane
I was glad to say goodbye to my splendid carriage.
But this mid-summer a high wind blew without ceasing,
My humble dwelling burst into sudden flame.

In all the house not a rafter was left in the roof,
And now I live in a boat in front of the door.
Long, long is this early autumn evening,
High, so high is the moon, and almost full.
The fruits and plants of my garden are growing again,
But the frightened crows have not come back to their nests.
It is midnight, and here I stand, with my thoughts ranging,
And gaze all round and above at the depths of the sky.
Even in childhood I held my thoughts aloof,
And thus have I been for more than forty years.
My body follows the simple pattern of Nature,
My spirit ever remains alone and idle.
I have become so self-reliant and strong
That jade and stone are not so hard as I am.
I look up and think of Dong Hu's* times of old,
When the people threw the surplus grain in the fields.
And, eating their fill, they had no more cares in the world
Than to rise in the morning and in the evening sleep.
But now since the times are not in the least like those,
I had better begin to water my western garden!

Moving Home

There's many a fine day here in spring and in autumn
When I love to climb the hill and compose new verses.

---

* A legendary king.

I never pass a gate but somebody greets me;
If a man has wine he shares it with all around.
When work in the fields is done, each one goes home;
And then at leisure I think again of friends.
I think of friends — and fling my cloak on my shoulder
For never we tire of talk and laughter together.
So are not all these things good reasons enough
Why I should not depart from this place?
But food and clothes must needs be won for a living;
My strong hand on the plough will never fail me.

Harvesting Early Rice in the West Field in the Ninth Month of the Year Gengxu (AD 410)

There are many sides indeed to human life,
Food and clothing are necessaries.
It is not so easy to toil to obtain these
And yet to seek for peace within oneself.
With the spring my round of labour begins anew
And I can look ahead to my yearly harvest.
Out with the dawn, exerting all my strength,
Home at sundown bearing my plough on my shoulder.
In the hills there is either frost or there is dew,
The very air and the wind are colder here.
How can it not be hard, this farmer's life?
And the hardship is such that no one can avoid.

So tired is my whole body when I come home,
That I cannot even think of other troubles.
I bath, and then I rest beneath my eaves,
And a jar of wine scatters my cares away.
It is long, so long, since the time of Ju and Ni, *
A thousand years part us, and yet we are one.
If only my life could always be like this!
I don't complain of dragging my own plough.

Miscellaneous Poems

The sun has sunk in the depths of the western river,
The pure moon rises over the eastern hills.
In its thousand-league beams the vast scene
Far, far around me shimmers on the air.
A wind is rising and blows in at my windows,
And now at night the pillows and sheets are cold.
The change in the air tells me what season it is,
Sleepless, I know too well that the nights are long.
I want to talk, but there's no one for me to talk to,
I raise my cup and drink to my lonely shadow.
Oh, days and months — how they waste us all away!
I had ideals, and I have not fulfilled them!
This is the thought that obsesses me with its sadness
And all night long will rob me of my calm.

---

* Legendary hermit farmers.

I remember that in my young days,
If I had no reason for joy, yet still was I happy.
My brave ambitions embraced the whole world,
My winged imagination soared far.
But suddenly the months and years have gone by,
And this heart of mine is partly spent already.
Though joy is within my grasp, yet it gives me no pleasure,
Anxiety and sadness are ever my mood.
Little by little my physical strength declines,
I begin to feel the times are not what they were.
My "boat in the cave" may soon be "stolen away". *
I am carried along on a stream, and I cannot stop.
How much more of my journey is left to go?
Where shall I anchor at last? I cannot tell.
The men of old treasured each moment of time,
But I, when I think on these things, I am afraid!

I never wished to receive an official's pay,
The fields and the mulberry trees are my profession.
I work myself, there's no one to take my place,
Sometimes in hunger and cold I have eaten chaff.
I do not hope to eat my bellyful,
All I desire is enough to assuage hunger.
In the winter I manage with rough cloth of cotton.
The coarsest hemp must do for the summer sun;

---

* In a fable of Zhuangzi a man hid his boat in a deep cave and thought it was secure; but when night came a strong man found the boat and carried it away. The moral is that if your time has come, however careful of yourself you are, it is no use.

And even these I often cannot obtain.
Alas! What pain it is that of all mankind,
Who constantly strive to gain their heart's desire,
This foolish scholar should so fail in his!
But what's to be done? That is the way things are,
So let me drink a single cup and be happy.

Poems on Drinking Wine

I am not really happy living without work; moreover, the nights are growing long. So when I manage, as I occasionally do, to procure some famous wine, not a night passes without my drinking deep. Here I sit, alone with my shadow and emptying my glass; then, all of a sudden — I am drunk! After I have reached that point, I often start writing a few lines for fun. Though I consume much paper and ink, what I write has very little sense, but I have asked my old friend to copy out these poems in the hope that they may at least be amusing.

I have built my cottage amongst the throng of men,
And yet there is no noise of horse and of carriage.
You ask me, how can it be? and I reply:
When my heart is absent the place itself is absent;
For I pick chrysanthemums under the eastern hedge,
And far away to the south I can see the mountains,
And the mountain mists are lovely at morning and evening,

While birds keep flying across and back again.
In all these things there lies a profound meaning.
I was going to explain... but now I forget what it was.

Lovely is the colour of the autumn chrysanthemum,
When you gather its flowers that are all wet with dew!
Let the Reliever of Sorrows overflow,
And carry my feelings far away from the world.
Though I am alone and broach but a single jar,
When my cup is empty the wine-pot pours itself.
It is evening and all activity is ceasing,
The calling birds are returning home to the woods,
And I am at ease at a window facing the west.
Once more I attain to the full enjoyment of life.

My old friends come to see me to give me pleasure,
So, lifting the wine-jar, we set forth together.
We clear the brambles, sit beneath a pine,
Pour a few cupfuls — then we are drunk again,
The elders now are off in endless chatter,
And we have lost count of how many cups we have filled.
I cannot even be sure if this is myself.
How can I tell any more the important issues?
Far, far have I left the world behind.
Surely in wine there lies a joy profound!

Xi and Nong* are far away in time;

---

* Legendary emperors. Fu Xi was said to have introduced writing and Shen Nong agriculture.

Rare indeed today is truth like theirs.
The Old Man of Lu, * persistent, tireless,
Patched up the world and made it whole again,
And though the phoenix would not return to the land
Music and virtue were, for a time, renewed —
The rivers of Shu and Si** their whisper ceased,
Yet they flowed and floated on to the cruel Qin. ***
What crime had ever been done by the Classical Books
That they should be turned in a day to dust and ashes?
Those few old men, that tiny band of scholars,
Their action then was truly devoted and great —
Why has this greatness so died out in the world
That nobody cares any more for the Six Classics?
I could travel as far as a whole day's journey by coach
And not see a man who would ask me so much as a question.
Quick! Let me drink again, for if I don't
I shall feel I do not deserve my scholar's hat.
If my uncouth expressions cause you offence
I beg that you will forgive a drunken man.

---

* Confucius. He regretted that the phoenix was no more to be seen in the world, which he said
   was because the world was in chaos.

** Rivers on the banks of which Confucius once taught his students.

*** The First Emperor of Qin (221-210 BC), unifier of China and builder of the Great Wall,
   typified by the poet, and throughout Chinese literature, as the supreme tyrant, burnt the
   Confucian classics in his drive to found a new form of centralized state. Knowing the classics
   by heart, a few old scholars fled to remote regions till the reign of Qin was over, when they
   returned to dictate the classics anew and so preserved them.

Plaint , to the Melody of Chu: Written for Mr Pang and Mr Deng

Heaven is unfathomable, Heaven is distant.
Mysterious are the ways of gods and demons!

When I was young I dreamed of noble deeds,
But for fifty years all I have done is to labour.
I met with troubles since first I grew up.
So soon after I wed her I lost my beloved!
Fire has more than once burnt down my cottage,
Pests have ravaged through my fields at their pleasure,
Wind and rain have struck them from all directions.
My harvest is too little for one man,
Often I go hungry on summer days,
And on winter nights sleep without blankets;
In the early evening I think of cockcrow,
When morning comes I long for sundown.
It is my own fate — why blame Heaven?
Parting, hardship and sorrow confront me always.
And as for glory after I am gone,
Why, it is no more to me than drifting smoke!
To you, my friends, I am singing my sad song
To you who alone understand, like the sage Zhong Ziqi.

Songs of a Poor Scholar

Cold and harsh comes in the evening of the year.
Wrapped in rough hemp I sun myself in the porch.
Nothing is growing now in the southern orchard,
In the northern garden the branches all are bare,
The last drop has been poured out from the winepot,
I look at my kitchen hearth and I see no smoke.
The books are pushed away in the side of the chair;
Midday is past, and I've still no heart to read them.
I have no work, unlike the Master at Chen,*
Privately, anxiously questioned in his distress.
What comfort can I find to strengthen my heart?
The fact that of old there was many a sage like this.

Peach-Blossom Springs

In the Taiyuan period** of the Jin Dynasty, there was a man of
Wuling*** who was a fisherman by trade. One day he was fishing
up a stream in his boat, and heedless of how far he had gone,
when suddenly he came upon a forest of peach trees. On both

---

* Confucius and a disciple, when travelling through the State of Chen could not obtain food
and suffered acutely. The disciple's anxious question was: "Can a man of honour be conquered by hunger?" Confucius' answer was: "The man of honour can bear hunger, while the
vulgar under the stress of hunger will do anything."

** AD 376-396.

*** In Hunan Province.

banks for several hundred yards there were no other kinds of trees. The fragrant grass was delicious and beautiful to look at, all patterned with fallen blossom. The fisherman was extremely surprised and went on further, determined to get to the end of this wood.

He found the end of the wood and the source of the stream together, at the foot of a cliff, and in this cliff there was a small cave in which there seemed to be a faint light. He left his boat and went in through the mouth of the cave. At first it was very narrow, only just wide enough for a man, but after forty or fifty yards he suddenly found himself in the open.

The place he had come to was level and spacious. There were houses and cottages arranged in a planned order; there were fine fields and beautiful pools; there were mulberry trees, bamboo groves, and many other kinds of trees as well; there were raised pathways round the fields; and he heard the sound of chickens and of dogs. Going to and fro in all this, and busied in working and planting, were people, both men and women. Their dress was not unlike that of people outside, but all of them, whether old people with white hair or children with their hair tied in a knot, all were happy and content with themselves.

When they saw the fisherman they were greatly amazed and asked him where he had come from. He answered all their questions, and then they asked him back to their homes, where they put wine before him, killed chickens and prepared food in his honour. When the other people in the village heard about the visitor, they too all came to ask questions.

They themselves told him that their ancestors had escaped

from the wars and confusion in the time of the Qin Dynasty. *
Bringing their wives and children, all the people of their district
had reached this inaccessible place, and never again had they left
it. Thus they had lost all contact with the world outside. They
asked what dynasty it was now. They had never even heard of
the Han, let alone the Wei and the Jin. Point by point the fisherman explained all he could of the world that he knew, and they
all sighed in deep sorrow.

Afterwards all the rest began again to ask him to their homes,
and all feasted him with wine and food. He stayed there several
days and then bade them goodbye; but before he departed these
people said to him: "Never speak to anyone outside about this!"

So he went out, found his boat and went back by the same
route as he had come; but all along the way he left marks; and
when he got to the provincial town he called on the prefect and
told him all about his experience. The prefect at once sent men
to go with him and follow up the marks he had left. But they became completely confused over the marks and never succeeded in
finding the way.

A scholar from Nanyang, a man of high reputation named Liu
Ziji, heard of the affair and enthusiastically offered to go out
with the fisherman to try again. But this, too, came to nothing,
for he fell ill and died. After that no one went any more to look
for the stream.

> The Qin Emperor threw the world in confusion,
> Good men fled from his times and his dominion.

---

* 221-207 BC.

Huang and his friends reached the Shang Mountain,

And these others fled away too and escaped;

All trace of their journey vanished for ever,

And the path they trod was covered with grass and deserted.

Their living they gain by tilling the soil and reaping;

When the sun goes down they go to rest together.

Bamboo and mulberry bend to give them shade,

Beans and rice follow at seasons due.

From the spring silkworm they gather long thread,

At the autumn harvest there is no imperial tax.

The only lanes are made by their coming and going,

Cocks are crowing and dogs are barking together.

The rites are all performed in the ancient manner,

And in their clothes there are no new fashions.

Children run and sing to their hearts' content,

The grey-haired happily go round visiting friends.

The flowering grass tells them what month it is.

They know the autumn wind by the bare branches;

For even without a calendar to show you

The four seasons still add up to a year.

At peace together, they live in abounding joy;

What need have they to cudgel their brains and scheme?

Five hundred years they had lain thus strangely hidden,

When there came a man to disclose this magic world;

But since good and evil spring from different sources,

When he had gone it returned to its mystery.

You men of the world, what can you know, may I ask,
Of things so far beyond your noise and your dust?
But for me, I long to rise on the gentle wind,
To be soaring high and searching for my friends.

Reading the *Classic of Seas and Mountains*

It is early summer, the flowers and plants are growing,
Around my house are spreading wide the trees
In which a host of birds find happy refuge;
And I as well, I love my thatched cottage.
I have done my ploughing and I have done my planting,
Now I have leisure again to read my books.
Our rustic lane is small for a grand carriage,
But my old friend's cart is always coming and going.
In a merry mood we pour out the spring wine,
And together we pick the vegetables in the garden.
A fine rain is coming in from the east,
And a sweet breeze is blowing along with it,
I glance at the *Tales of the Immortal King of Zhou*
And the illustrations to the *Classic of Seas and Mountains*.
Looking up and down, I survey the universe;
How can I not, yet once again, be happy?

Song to Jing Ke [*]

The Prince of Yan, generous patron of talent,
Burnt for revenge against the tyrant of Qin.
He gathered round him a hundred good men;
At the close of the year he enlisted noble Jing.
A man of honour is willing to die for his friend,
So, raising his sword, he left the Yan city,
And his white charger neighed on the broad road.
Chivalrously he bade them all farewell;
His tall hat bristled from his hero's hair,
And its tassel was streaming up in his fierce breath.
They drank farewell on the banks of the waters of Yi
At a feast where heroes crowded round every table,
Jian Li mournfully struck the lute,
While Song Yi sang with ringing tones.
The sad wind's sighing died down,
The cold waves whispered, quietly breaking.
A solemn note took the place of tears,
A martial note alerted the strong men.
They knew in their hearts that he would never return,
But only his fame pass on to future ages.
He mounted his carriage and never turned his head;
Flying it vanished towards the palace of Qin.
Furiously he journeyed a myriad miles,

---

[*] Jing Ke, on behalf of his patron the Prince of Yan, made an unsuccessful attempt to assassi-
nate the First Emperor of Qin in 227 BC. He evaded the prohibition on weapons in the
emperor's presence by concealing a sword in a rolled-up map.

Winding his way he passed a thousand cities.
The thing should have happened when the map was unrolled
    to its end,
But the cruel lord was nervous and on his guard.
Oh! Pity it was that his skill should be just too little,
And therefore the great deed fail its fulfilment!
Although this man is already so long dead,
For a thousand years our love for him will endure.

Begging for Food

Famine came and drove me to leave home,
But after all, where was there to go?
On and on, till I came to this street.
I knocked on a door but was too ashamed to speak.
The owner of the house understood it all.
He called me in, and I had not come in vain!
All the day and all that night we talked
And dined and drained our cups time after time.
We talked, we sang, we fell to exchanging poems,
Happy in celebrating our new friendship.
I feel you are kind as the washerwoman of old, *
Though I, alas, am no hero General Han.
Deeply touched, I can only give you thanks;
Repayment must be made elsewhere by Heaven.

---

* A washerwoman gave a bowl of rice to General Han Xin (c. 200 BC) when he was poor and hungry. When he later became the Prince of Chu he remembered her and rewarded her with gold.

My Funeral Song

Lonely the vast expanse of withered grass,
Whispering, sighing, the white poplar* leaves!
There's bitter frost now in this autumn month,
When they've brought me here out of the town so far.
No one lives near this place,
Only the tall mounds stand up around —
A horse looks up at the sky and neighs,
The wind itself blows desolately.
When that dark room is once closed,
In a thousand years I'll never see out again,
In a thousand years, never see out again!
Virtue and wisdom are no avail whatever.
Those who have come here to see me off
Will soon return, each to his own home;
Relations perhaps will be sorry a little longer,
The others will merely finish the chant and go.
Dead and gone — there's nothing more to be said —
My body I now entrust to be mingled with the hills.

Translated by Andrew Boyd

---

* Commonly grown on graveyards.

Returning Home

My family were poor and we barely scraped a living from our farm. Our home was crowded with children and there was never enough grain to feed them. I did not know how to provide for them. Friends and relatives urged me to accept some official position, and I felt persuaded to do so, although I could not see how to get one. Wars affected different parts of the country and the governors of the various districts were eager to enlist talented men in their service. An uncle, aware of my poverty, offered me a job in a small town, but because there was so much unrest, I feared the thought of travelling to such a distant place. Pengze County, however, was only a hundred *li* from my home. What I would earn there would be sufficient to keep me in wine, so I applied for the post. After a short time, I began to wish I was back home. My temperament comes from nature. I cannot be a hypocrite. Cold and hunger are hard to bear, but acting contrary to one's nature is even harder. When I applied for that post I was a slave to my belly. I deeply regretted my action and decided to leave immediately after the harvest. When my younger sister, who had married into the Cheng family, died in Wuchang, I wanted to gallop there at once, so I resigned my post. I had filled it for little more than eighty days, from mid-autumn to winter. Pleased with my decision, I wrote this poem, *Returning Home*. Now it is the eleventh month of the year Yisi (AD 405).

Again to home I long to turn.
Weeds choke my fields, why not return?

Serving my body, my heart became a slave;

Why should I mourn and life be so grave?

I know that to regret the past is vain;

But I can still use the years that remain.

I lost my way, but not too far astray;

Now I act aright through mistakes of yesterday.

Gently rocking, far my small boat goes;

On my clothes a light breeze blows.

A passer-by I ask to point my way;

Sad that I must await the dawn of day.

When in the distance my home appears in sight;

I start to run, filled with delight.

My slaves and servants come in greeting;

At the door, my children wait our meeting.

Overgrown with weeds, the paths almost disappear,

Yet the pine tree and chrysanthemums are here.

Into a room, my children I guide;

A full jug of wine I find inside.

Pouring the wine, my cup I raise,

And on my courtyard's tree with pleasure gaze.

Leaning on my southern sill, enjoying peace of mind,

I learn that in this simple place, contentment I find.

Each day in my garden, new pleasures wait,

Yet my home is closed, despite the gate.

Cane in hand, my leisured course I tread;

Gazing far, I sometimes raise my head.

Among the hills, the clouds drift without aim;

Birds, tired in flight, return home again.

The scene darkens with the setting of the sun;

Caressing a lonely pine, I linger on.

To my home I must return;
To sever all ties I yearn;
Since the world and I are at variance set,
Why seek more desire or more regret?
Family conversations I most enjoy;
Pleasure in my books, or with the lute I toy.
The peasants tell me that spring is at hand;
So I must now prepare my western land.
Sometimes for my coach with curtains drawn I go,
Sometimes in my boat alone I row.
Via winding ways I reach some vale;
Via rugged routes some hill I scale.
With joy the budding trees seem to grow;
The murmuring streams again begin to flow.
The timeliness of nature makes me glad;
The shortness of my life makes me sad.
Alas, alas!
How long before my earthly form must pass?
Yet following my heart and banishing care,
I should do what? I should go where?
Riches and rank are not what I desire;
Nor to some paradise do I aspire.
Alone, I stroll about each fine day,
Taking my hoe to cut the weeds away.
Climbing the eastern hill, I'll sing in delight,

Or beside some clear stream, a poem I'll recite.
In harmony with nature, my end I await;
Quietly content, why question fate?

Translated by Yang Xianyi
and Gladys Yang

The Bride of Jiao Zhongqing

THIS is one of the longest of the ancient ballads and is part of the *yuefu* folk-song corpus. Its genesis is recounted by Xu Ling of the Chen Dynasty (AD 557-589) in the preface to his *New Songs from the Jade Terrace* in these words:

> Jiao Zhongqing was a local official in the prefecture of Lu-jiang during the reign of Jianan (AD 196-219) in the Eastern Han Dynasty. His wife Liu was sent away by his mother and vowed never to marry again. Compelled by her family to break her vow, she had no recourse but to drown herself in a pond, on receipt of which news Jiao Zhongqing hanged himself in his courtyard. The long poem was composed by contemporaries in their memory.

The final version had evidently been elaborated orally during the intervening centuries.

The Bride of Jiao Zhongqing

Southeast the lovelorn peacock flies. Alack,
At every mile she falters and looks back!

At thirteen years Lanzhi learned how to weave;
At fourteen years she could embroider, sew;
At fifteen music on her lute she made;
At sixteen knew the classics, prose and verse.
At seventeen they wed her to Zhongqing,
And from that day what joy and pain were hers!
As work kept Zhongqing in the yamen far,
His absence made her love the deeper still.
She started weaving at the dawn of day,
Worked at the loom until the midnight hour.
The tapestries beneath her fingers grew,
Yet Zhongqing's mother sore berated her —
Not for poor work or any tardy pace,
But she was mistress: brides must know their place.

At length in sorrow to Zhongqing she said,
"If I have failed to serve your mother well,
Useless to stay... Please go and tell her so.
Should she think fit, I fain would go away."
The husband, shame-faced, on this errand went.
"Mother," he said, "no lordly post is mine.
To wed Lanzhi was more than I deserved.
As man and wife we love each other so

That naught but death itself shall sever us.
Less than three years have we been wedded now;
Our life together is a budding flower.
Lanzhi, methinks, has done her best, no less.
Why treat her, then, with such unkindliness?"

To which the shrewish mother made reply,
"Dull are your wits and foolish, O my son!
Your wife lacks graces and she lacks good sense.
See her for what she is, self-willed and vain.
The very sight of her offends my eyes.
I wonder that you dare to plead her cause!
A proper wife I have in mind for you...
Yonder she lives, a maid called Qin Luofu,
A matchless beauty she, upon my word,
And I have ways to compass her consent.
Now listen! We must get your slut away!
Yes, go must she, and go without delay!"

For filial piety he knelt him down,
And pitiful yet firm was his appeal.
"Mother, if 'tis your will, cast out Lanzhi,
But do not think that I will marry twice!"
At this the mother's fury knew no bounds.
She ranted wildly, strumming on her stool:
"Is reverence for aged parents dead?
Defend a wife and flout a mother's wish?
This stranger in the house I will not bear,
And none henceforth to thwart my will shall dare!"

Zhongqing fell dumb before his mother's rage,
Made her a bow profound and went his way.
In tears and sorrow he sought poor Lanzhi,
Though little comfort for them both he knew.
"The thought of parting rends my heart in twain!
And yet my mother will not be gainsaid.
My duties at the yamen call me hence.
'Tis best you go back to your brother's home.
My yamen tasks complete, I will return
And take you with me to our home again.
It has to be, alas! Forgive me now,
And doubt not I will keep my solemn vow!"

"Nay, make no care to come for me again.
'Twas in the depth of winter, I recall,
I first came to this house a timid bride.
I bore myself with filial reverence,
Was never obstinate, self-willed or rude.
For three years, day and night, I toiled for her,
Nor recked how long that sorry state might last.
My only care to serve your mother's will
And to repay the love you bore to me.
Yet from this house I now am driven out...
To what avail to bring me back again?
I'll leave my broidered jacket of brocade,
(Its golden lacings still are fresh and bright,)
My small, soft canopy of scarlet gauze
With perfumed herbs sewn in its corners four.
My trunks, my dowry, too, I leave behind,

As fair as ever in their silken wraps —
Things, some of them, I had a fancy for,
Though now neglected and untouched they lie.
True, they are only cheap and tawdry wares,
Not nearly good enough for your new bride.
But you may share them out as tiny gifts,
Or, if you find no fit occasion now,
Keep them, my dear," she said, her eyes all wet,
"And her who owned them do not quite forget."

When the loud cock-crow marked another day
Lanzhi arose betimes and dressed herself.
She put on her embroidered skirt of silk,
And silken slippers pleasing to the eye,
Studded her braided locks with jewellery,
Hung pearly ear-rings in her little ears,
With touch so delicate applied the rouge
Until her lips, already perfect, glowed.
Her fingers had a tapering loveliness,
Her waist seemed like a many-coloured cloud.
A peerless beauty did she look, and sweet
The grace with which she moved her little feet.

To Zhongqing's mother then she bade farewell
In tender words that found a churlish ear:
"Lady, I am of humble origin,
Not well-instructed and not well brought-up.
Stupid and shallow and inept am I —
A sorry mate for any noble heir.

Yet you have treated me with kindliness,
And I, for shame, I have not served you well.
This house for evermore today I leave,
And that I cannot serve you more I grieve."

Then, with the warm tears trickling down her cheeks,
She bade farewell to Zhongqing's sister dear:
"When to this house I first came as a bride,
Dear sister, you were just a naughty child.
See you have grown well nigh as tall as I.
Now I must bid a hasty, long farewell;
Yet, if you love me, sister, for my sake,
Be gentle to your mother, care for her.
When all the maidens hold their festivals,
Forget not her who once looked after you."
With blinding tears and with a heavy heart
She took her seat then in the waiting cart.

For fear of prying eyes and cruel tongues
Zhongqing would meet her where the four roads met.
On the rough road her carriage pitched and shook,
The wheel-rims clattered and the axle creaked.
Then suddenly a horseman galloped up,
Down leaped the rider eagerly — 'twas he!
They sat together and he whispered low:
"My love shall last to all eternity!
Only a short while with your brother stay,
The little while my yamen duties take.
Then I'll come back... Let not your heart be sore!

I'll claim you for my very own once more!"

Poor Lanzhi, sobbing, fondly plucked his sleeve.
"Oh, what a comfort to me is your love!
And if you cannot bear to give me up,
Then come, but come before it is too late!
Be your love strong, enduring as the rocks!
Be mine resistant as the creeping vine!
For what is tougher than the creeping vine?
And what more fixed than the eternal rocks?
Yet when I think upon my brother, lord
And tyrant of his household, then I fear
He will not look on me with kindliness,
And I shall suffer from his rage and scorn."
At length in tears the loving couple parted,
And lengthening distance left them broken-hearted.

When Lanzhi, all unheralded, reached home,
Doubt and suspicion clouded every mind.
"Daughter!" Her mother in amazement cried.
"Alas! What brings you unattended back?
At thirteen, I recall, you learned to weave;
At fourteen years you could embroider, sew;
At fifteen, music on the lute you made;
At sixteen knew the classics, prose and verse.
And then at seventeen, a lovely bride...
How proud I was to see you prosper so!
Yet, dear, you must have erred in deed or word.
Tell me the cause of your return alone."

Said Lanzhi, "Truly I am brought full low,
Yet in my duty did I never fail."
The mother wept for pity at her tale.

Upon the tenth day after her return
There came one from the county magistrate,
A go-between, to woo her for his son,
A lad who had bare twenty summers seen,
Whose good looks put all other youths to shame,
Whose tongue was fluent and full eloquent.
Her mother, hoping against hope, said, "Child,
I pray you, if it pleases you, consent."
To which, in tears again, Lanzhi replied:
"Dear mother, when I parted with Zhongqing
He said, 'Be faithful!' o'er and o'er again,
And we both vowed eternal constancy.
If I should break my word and fickle prove,
Remorse would haunt me till my dying day.
I pray you tell the marriage-maker so."

So to the go-between the mother said:
"O honoured sir, a stubborn child is mine,
But lately sent back to her brother's house.
A small official found her no good match —
How should she please the magistrate's own heir?
Besides, she is in melancholy state:
Young gentlemen require a gayer mate."

So the official go-between went off

And, ere reporting to the magistrate,
Found for the spring another fitting maid,
Born of a nearby family of note;
And, haply meeting with the prefect's scribe,
Learned that His Excellency's son and heir,
A worthy, excellent and handsome youth,
Himself aspired to wed the fair Lanzhi.
So to the brother's house they came once more,
This time as envoys from the prefect sent.
The flowery, official greetings o'er,
They told the special reason they had come.
The mother, torn this way and that, declared:
"My child has vowed she ne'er will wed again.
I fear I know no way to change her mind."
But Lanzhi's brother, ever worldy-wise,
Was never slow to seize a heaven-sent chance,
And to his sister spoke blunt words and harsh:
"See you not, girl, how much this profits you?
Your former husband held a petty post.
Now comes an offer from the prefect's son:
A greater contrast would be hard to find.
Turn down this offer if you will, this prize,
But think not I shall find your daily rice!"

What must be, must be, then thought poor Lanzhi.
"Brother," she said, "what you have said is good.
I was a wife and now am none again;
I left you once and then came back again
To dwell beneath your hospitable roof.

Your will is such as cannot be gainsaid.
True, to Zhongqing I gave my plighted word,
Yet faint the hope of seeing him again!
Your counsel I must welcome as a boon:
Pray you, arrange the ceremony soon."

When he heard this, the official go-between
Agreed to everything the brother asked.
Then to the prefect's house they hurried back
To tell the happy outcome of their work.
It seemed so good a marriage for his son,
The prefect thought, that full of sheer delight
He turned the pages of the almanac,
And therein found the most auspicious date
To be the thirtieth of that same month.
Whereon he summoned his subordinates:
"The thirtieth is a heaven-favoured day,"
Said he, "and that is but three days ahead.
Have all in readiness to greet the bride."
The household was abuzz from floor to roof
As was befitting for a noble match.
There were, to fetch the bride, gay gondolas
Fresh-painted with designs of lucky birds
And silken pennants fluttering o'er the deck.
There were gold carriages with jade inlay
And well-groomed horses of the finest breed
With saddles shining, harness all bedight!
As for the presents, strings of cash they told
Three thousand, pieces of brocade and silk
Three hundred. And among those precious gifts
Were globe-fish brought from some far distant clime.

The welcoming cortege, five hundred strong,
Would gladden all eyes as it passed along.

In the bride's house the troubled mother said:
"Lanzhi, the prefect's messengers have come.
The welcoming party will arrive full soon.
'Tis time you donned your bridal finery.
You have agreed... No time to tarry now!"
Lanzhi, too sad to utter any word,
Sobbed neath her kerchief to conceal her grief,
Her pale, pale cheeks all wet with bitter tears.
She dragged a chair with heavy marble seat
Towards the window where there was more light,
Took silk and scissors, measure, needle, braid,
Cut out in grief and wet her thread with tears.
Ere noon a jacket new and skirt she made;
By eve a wedding gown was all complete.
Then in the twilight, desperate, forlorn,
Out at the gate she stole to weep alone.
Then, suddenly, her sobbing died away...
Far off she heard a horse's anguished neigh!
Oh, that familiar neigh! Yet why so sore?
Indeed Zhongqing was riding fast that way.
The master had heard news, lost heart, asked leave.
The very steed, too, his forebodings shared.
At last, her straining eyes perceived him clear:
His presence filled her with both joy and pain.
Patting the horse, she heaved a woeful sigh.
"Zhongqing, my darling, at our parting dire
None could foresee the course events would take.
You cannot guess my abject misery,

But all we hoped is now an empty dream.
My mother you knew well. My tyrant brother,
'Twas he who schemed to wed me to another.
Now that the die is cast by fate austere,
What more can you expect of me, my dear?"

Zhongqing, heart-stricken, forced himself to say,
"May you know every happiness, Lanzhi!
The rock stands fixed, unyielding evermore,
But oh! I fear the fibres of the vine
Have lost their toughness all too easily...
May you be rich and live in happy state,
But as for me, why, death shall be my fate!"
That stung her to the quick, but she replied,
"Why say such cruel things to me, my dear?
We both are shipwrecked on the sea of life,
Our vessels foundered by the ruthless gale.
Life has enjoined that man and wife must sever:
Let us both die, and be one flesh for ever!"

Long hand in hand they stayed before they went
With mournful steps and slow their several ways —
Two lovers, parting, knowing all too well
That death alone could make them one again.
All roads to joy fast blocked, they did not quail,
But vowed to terminate their tragic tale.

When Zhongqing, heavy-hearted, reached his home,
Straight to his mother's room he went, and bowed.

"The weather changes, mother. Bitter cold,
A terrifying wind sears leaf and tree.
The frost congeals the orchids, all the flowers,
And Zhongqing's life, too, draws unto its close.
His sole regret is leaving you alone,
But 'tis his own desire to end life so —
No ghost, no devil, mother, holds him thrall!
Your son is like the rocks of Nanshan Range,
Immutable in death, immune to change."

The mother heard these words in sore amaze,
But guessed their cause, and pitied him in tears.
"My son, sole heir of noble family,
What great and glorious prospects lie ahead!
Why for a wanton should you think to die,
One so inferior in every way?
As I have told you, in the neighbourhood
There dwells a paragon of loveliness.
Soon will I send a go-between to her,
And long and happy years be yours, my son!"

But he kept silence, bowed right low, and left,
Long, long his empty room he paced, and thought
A myriad thoughts of Lanzhi, love, and death.
Oft glanced he sadly towards his mother's room;
The world seemed shrouded in a pall of gloom!

The day for Lanzhi's splendid wedding came,
She lonelier than ever mid the throng.

She waited, waited till the night should fall.
At last the turmoil ceased, the guests thinned out.
"This is the day," she mused, "my journey's end.
My soul will wander, though my corse remain."
The pond's dark waters beckoned, cold and chill.
Barefoot she waded in, and all was still.
Though for the news Zhongqing was half-prepared,
It nowise lighter made the dreadful blow.
Beneath the courtyard trees release he sought,
Turned him southeast, and then the rope went taut...

Linked in a common grief, the families
Buried the lovers fond on Mount Huashan.
And all around the graveyard grow dark pines,
Through all the changing seasons ever green,
With cypress interspersed and *wutong* trees.
Like loving arms the branches intertwine,
And lovingly the leaves and sprays caress;
And in the foliage dwell two little birds,
That mate for life, whose very name is love.
They cross their bills and sing to one another
Their soft endearments all night long till dawn,
And passers-by stand spellbound at the sound,
And lonely widows wake to hear and muse
Upon this story of a bygone day
Which shall endure till all shall pass away.

Translated by Eric Edney
and Cao Dun

A Selection of Early Ghost and Fairy Stories

THESE 25 stories have been taken from the collections *Tales of Marvels*, *Records of Spirits*, *Records of Ghosts and Spirits*, *More Records of Spirits*, *Records of Light and Darkness*, *Supplementary Tales of Qi*, *Records of Mysterious Manifestations* and *Accounts of Avenging Spirits*.

Tales of Marvels is attributed to Cao Pi (AD 187-226) of the Wei-dynasty ruling family, but most of its stories are additions by others.

Records of Spirits is attributed to Gan Bao, a historian of the Eastern Jin Dynasty (AD 317-420). The preface says that the stories were collected to prove the existence of spirits.

Records of Ghosts and Spirits was written by one named Xun, who probably lived at the same time as or a little later than Gan Bao.

More Records of Spirits is ascribed to the poet Tao Yuanming.

Records of Light and Darkness is attributed to the Song-dynasty prince Liu Yiqing (AD 403-444), a prominent patron of letters.

Supplementary Tales of Qi was written by Wu Jun (AD 469-520), an eminent scholar under the Liang Dynasty.

Records of Mysterious Manifestations is attributed to the Buddhist monk Wang Yan, born in Taiyuan in the fifth century, who is supposed to have written the book after witnessing two miracles.

Accounts of Avenging Spirits is the work of Yan Zhitui of the Northern Qi Dynasty (AD 550-577) in the north.

The Haunted House

Zhang Fen was a rich man of the principality of Wei. Suddenly falling into a decline, he sold his house to the Cheng family of Liyang. But after moving in, one after another they started falling ill and dying, so they in turn sold it to He Wen of Ye.

One evening He sat with drawn sword on the beam in the main hall facing south. At the second watch,* he saw a man over ten feet high in a tall hat and yellow garment come in.

"Slender Waist!" called this apparition. "Why do I smell a live man here?"

"There is no one," came the answer.

Then another in a tall hat and green came in, and after him another in a tall hat and white. Both asked the same question and received the same answer.

When it was nearly dawn, He came down and, addressing "Slender Waist" as they had, asked:

"Who is the one in yellow?"

"Gold," came the answer. "Under the west wall of the hall."

"Who is the one in green?"

"Copper, five paces from the well in front of the hall."

"Who is the one in white?"

"Silver, beneath the pillar in the northeast corner."

"And who are you?"

"I am a pestle under the stove."

At daybreak He dug as indicated, and found five hundred cat-

---

* About ten o'clock in the evening.

ties of gold, five hundred of silver, and more than ten million copper coins. When he burned the pestle the house ceased to be haunted.

The Man Who Sold a Ghost

When Zong Dingbo of Nanyang was young, he met a ghost one night as he was walking.

"Who are you?" he asked.

"A ghost, sir. Who are you?"

"A ghost like yourself," lied Zong.

"Where are you going?"

"To the city."

"So am I."

So they went on together for a mile or so.

"Walking is most exhausting. Why not carry each other in turn?" suggested the ghost.

"A good idea," agreed Zong.

First the ghost carried him for some distance.

"How heavy you are!" said the ghost. "Are you really a spectre?"

"I am a new ghost," answered Zong. "That is why I am heavier than usual."

Then he carried the ghost, who was no weight at all. And so they went on, changing several times.

"As I am a new ghost," said Zong presently, "I don't know what we spectres are most afraid of."

"Only human spittle," replied the ghost.

They went on together till they came to a stream, and Zong told the ghost to cross first, which he did without a sound. But when Zong crossed he made quite a splash.

"Why do you make a noise?" inquired the ghost.

"I only died recently," replied Zong. "I am not used to fording streams. You must excuse me."

As they approached the city, Zong threw the ghost over his shoulder and held him tight. The ghost gave a screech and begged to be put down, but Zong would not listen and headed straight for the market. When he put the ghost down it had turned into a goat, and he promptly sold it. But first he spat at it, to prevent its changing its form again. Then he left, the richer by one thousand five hundred coins.

So the saying spread:

Zong Dingbo did better than most —
Made money by selling a ghost.

The Prince of Suiyang's Daughter

A scholar named Tan was still unmarried at forty, which distressed him deeply. One night he was studying the *Book of Songs* at midnight when a girl of about sixteen came in. Her beauty and splendour had no equal on earth, and she offered to be his wife. She warned him, though:

"I am no ordinary woman, so for three years you must not look at me by torchlight."

They married and had a son, and when the boy was two years old, Tan could contain his curiosity no longer. While his wife lay asleep he stealthily held a torch over her. From the waist up she was flesh like anyone else, but from the waist down she was nothing but dry bones! Just then his wife woke up.

"You have wronged me, husband!" she cried. "I was soon to have become a mortal woman. Why couldn't you wait for one more year instead of holding that torch over me?"

Tan made abject apologies.

"Now we must part for ever," she said in tears. "You must take good care of my son. If you are too poor to support yourself, come with me now and I shall give you a present."

He followed her into a splendid hall — a rare building richly furnished — where she gave him a robe made of pearls.

"You can live on this," she told him.

And she tore a strip from his gown to leave there.

Later Tan sold the robe to the prince of Suiyang for ten million coins. As soon as the prince set eyes on it, he said:

"That was my daughter's robe. This fellow must be a grave-robber."

He had Tan tried, and refused to believe him when Tan described what had happened. But upon going to inspect the grave, they found it unbroken. And when they opened it, under the coffin lid they discovered the strip of Tan's garment. They perceived that his son resembled the princess too. So at last the prince was convinced. Summoning Tan, he returned him the robe and made him his son-in-law, while the child was recommended for a post in the palace guard.

The Jade Maiden

Xuan Chao was secretary in the provincial government of Jibei. During the Jiaping period* of the Wei Dynasty, he was sleeping alone one night when he dreamed that a goddess had come to him.

"I am a jade maiden from Heaven," she said, "a native of Dongjun named Chenggong. I lost my parents when I was a child, and the Heavenly Emperor, pitying my loneliness, has sent me to be your wife."

This dream was extremely vivid, and Xuan marvelled at her more than mortal beauty. When he awoke he longed for her as if she were close at hand. So three or four nights passed.

Then one day she came to visit him in person, riding in a curtained carriage with eight maids in attendance dressed in embroidered silks, as lovely as winged fairies. She told him she was seventy, but she looked like a girl of sixteen. In her carriage were a wine-pot and dishes, five pieces of pale green glassware. The food and wine were exquisite, and as she shared them with Xuan she said to him:

"I am a jade maiden from Heaven, sent to marry you. That is why I am here. It is not to repay former kindness, but because we were destined to be husband and wife. I cannot help you, but neither will I harm you. You can ride with me in swift carriages or on good steeds, you can share with me food and drink from distant lands, and always have clothes to wear. Since I am im-

---

* AD 249-253.

mortal I cannot bear you a son, but I will not be jealous of other women, and you can still marry according to the custom."

Thus they lived as husband and wife and she presented him with a poem which began as follows:

> Drifting high above fairy isles,
> I wander over rocks and clouds;
> The sacred herb grows without nourishment,
> And its great virtue lasts to eternity.
> Immortals do not descend to earth for nothing,
> But to help men according to fate;
> Accepting me will make your family prosper,
> Offending me will get you into trouble...

So the poem went on, but since it came to more than two hundred words we will not quote it all. She also made notes on the *Book of Change*,* attaching explanations to the hexagrams and sayings. These commentaries were logically reasoned and could also be used for divination, like Yang Xiong's *Tai Xuan* or Xue's *Zhong Jing*. Xuan could understand all her notes, and used them as oracles to divine the future.

When they had been married for seven or eight years, Xuan's parents found him a wife. Then the jade maiden came to feast and sleep with him on certain days, coming in the night and leaving in the morning as swiftly as if on wings. Only Xuan could see her. When he was alone people could hear talking, and her presence was felt though no one could actually see her. Later inquisi-

---

* An ancient classic containing oracles of the Zhou Dynasty.

tive friends questioned him, and the secret leaked out. Then the jade maiden took her leave of him.

"I am an immortal," she said. "I do not like others to know that I come to you. Now that you have been so careless and my secret is revealed, I shall not come back again. We have loved each other for many years, and now that we have to part, how can I help feeling sad? But what must be must be, so take good care of yourself!"

She bade her attendants bring wine and food, and took from a basket two sets of silk garments for him. She also gave him a poem. Then after a last embrace, they wept and parted. She mounted her carriage silently and left swiftly as the wind. For days Xuan pined for her and nearly fell ill.

Five years later, official business took Xuan to Luoyang. He was travelling west at the foot of Yu Mountain when he saw at a bend in the road a carriage with horses which looked like hers. When the carriage drew near, he found it indeed belonged to the jade maiden. She parted the curtains and they greeted each other with mingled joy and sorrow. Then she turned back and rode with him to Luoyang, where they lived together again and renewed their love. They were still together by the Taikang period* of the Jin Dynasty, but she did not come every day. Only on the third of the third month, the fifth of the fifth month, the seventh of the seventh month, the ninth of the ninth month, and the first and fifteenth of the tenth month would she come to stay

---

* AD 280-289.

for the night and leave the next morning. Inspired by this story, the scholar Zhang Hua* wrote a poem called *The Fairy Maid*.

Han Ping and His Wife

Han Ping, steward to Prince Kang of Song, married a beautiful daughter of the He family. But the prince took her from him. When he protested, he was imprisoned and sentenced to hard labour on the city wall. Then his wife secretly wrote to him to say:

> Rain, ceaseless rain,
> Great the river, deep the water,
> Yet there is sunrise in my heart.

This letter fell into the hands of the prince, who showed it to his followers, but no one could make out its meaning. Then the minister Su He said:

"The first line means that she is longing for him all the time, the second that they have no way of getting in touch, the third that she intends to take her life."

Then Han Ping killed himself.

His wife secretly tore her clothes. When the prince went up the tower with her, she threw herself from the top; and when his followers tried to seize her, her clothes tore away and she was dashed to death. On her belt she had left this message:

---

* A well-known scholar of the Jin Dynasty. This poem is lost.

"Your Highness wished me to live, but your servant chose to die. Please bury me with Han Ping."

The prince was angry and refused her request, ordering the local people to bury her in a separate grave.

"You speak of your endless love," said the prince. "If you can make these tombs come together, I will not stand in your way."

Then within one day two great catalpa trees sprang up above the two graves. In ten days they grew to an enormous size, and their branches inclined towards each other, their roots intertwined together beneath the soil, and their twigs interwound above. And two love birds, one male and one female, stayed on these trees, not departing morning or night. They billed and cooed most plaintively, and uttered heart-rending cries. The people of Song lamented the lovers' death and gave this tree the name "the tree of love". The southerners say the birds were the spirits of Han Ping and his wife. In Suiyang today there is a town named Han Ping, and people still sing of the lovers.

The Old Man and the Devils

Qin Jubo of the principality of Langya was sixty. One night after drinking, as he passed Pengshan Temple, he saw his two grandsons coming towards him. They took his arms and helped him along for about a hundred paces but then seized him by the neck and threw him to the ground.

"Old slave!" they swore. "You beat us up the other day, so today we are going to kill you."

Remembering that he had indeed beaten the boys some days ago, he pretended to be dead, and they left him alone. When he got home he decided to punish them. Shocked and distressed, the lads kowtowed to him.

"How could your own grandsons do such a thing?" they protested. "Those must have been devils. Please make another test."

He realized they were right.

A few days later the old man pretended to be drunk and walked past the temple again. Once more the two devils came to take his arms, and this time he seized them so that they could not escape. Reaching home, he put both devils on the fire, until their backs and bellies were scorched and cracked. He left them in the courtyard, and that night they escaped. Sorry that he had not killed them, about a month later the old man pretended to be drunk and went out at night again, taking a sword, unknown to his family. When he did not come back though it was very late, his grandsons were afraid that the devils might have caught him again, so they went to look for him. And this time the old man hacked his own grandsons to death.

The Serpent Sacrifice

In the province of Minzhong in Eastern Yue, Mount Yongling towers many miles high. In its northwest corner there was a huge serpent seventy to eighty feet long and so thick that it took a dozen men to encircle it. The local people went in terror of it, and many officers of Dongye and other adjoining districts were killed by it. Though they sacrificed oxen and sheep, they had no peace. Then someone dreamed — or some oracle predicted — that this serpent wanted to be fed with virgins of twelve or thirteen. The authorities were dismayed, but since the serpent continued to make trouble they began taking local girls to it, especially from the families of criminals. So every eighth month they made a morning sacrifice, setting down the girl at the mouth of the serpent's cave. And the serpent would come out to eat her.

This went on year after year until nine girls had been sacrificed this way. But when the order came down the tenth time, no girl could be found. Li Dan of Jiangle County had six daughters but no son, and his youngest daughter, Ji, offered to go. But her parents would not agree.

"My unhappy parents have six daughters only and no son," said Ji. "So they have no real descendant. We are not like Tiying* who was able to help her father. Since we cannot work to support them, but are simply a burden to them and no use at all, the sooner we die the better. Besides, my sale will bring in some money for my parents. Surely that is best!"

Still her parents could not bear to let her go. But in spite of this, Ji left home secretly. Having procured a sharp sword and a dog which could catch snakes, in the morning of the first day of the eighth month she went and sat down in the temple, taking her sword and her dog. She had first poured honey on several large rice cakes, which she put at the mouth of the cave, so presently the serpent came out. Its head was as big as a winnow-

---

* A girl in the Han Dynasty who offered to serve as a slave in place of her father.

ing fan, its eyes like bronze mirrors two feet in diameter. When it smelt the fragrant cakes and started eating them, Ji loosed her dog which began worrying the monster, while she cut and wounded it in several places from behind. In pain the serpent fled, writhing, but did not get far before it died. Then Ji went into the cave and found the skeletons of the nine girls. She carried them out and said sadly:

"Because you were timid, the serpent ate you, poor things!"

Then she made her way leisurely home.

When the prince of Yue heard this he made her his queen, appointed her father magistrate of Jiangle, and richly rewarded her mother and her sisters. Since then there have been no more monsters in Dongye, and the people have sung her praises to this day.

The Sword-Maker

Because Ganjiang Moya took three years to forge a pair of swords for the king of Chu, the king was angry and decided to kill him. One sword was male, the other female. Ganjiang's wife was about to give birth, and he said to her:

"I have taken three years to make these swords for the king, and he is angry. When I go there he will have me killed. If you give birth to a son, when he grows up tell him that if he goes out and faces the south hill he will see a pine growing on a stone with a sword in its back."

Then he took the female sword to the king. The king was in a rage, for he knew that there were two swords — one male and one female — and the female sword was here but not the male. So in a passion he killed the sword-maker.

Ganjiang's son was named Chi. When he grew up he asked his mother:

"Where is my father?"

"Your father took three years to make a pair of swords for the king of Chu," she told him. "The king was angry and killed him. But before he left home he bade me tell you that if you go out and face the south hill, you will find a pine growing on a stone with a sword in its back."

The son went out and faced south, but he saw no hill. All he saw was a pillar of pine wood on a stone base before the hall. He cut this open with his axe and found the sword. Then day and night he thirsted for revenge.

The king saw in a dream a boy with a brow one foot across who wanted to take revenge on him. He offered a reward of a thousand gold pieces for him. And when Chi heard this he fled lamenting to the mountains. There a stranger accosted him.

"You are young," he said. "Why should you wail so bitterly?"

"I am the son of Ganjiang Moya," replied the lad. "The king of Chu killed my father, and I want revenge."

"I hear the king has offered a reward of a thousand gold pieces for your head," said the stranger. "Give me your head and your sword, and I will avenge you."

"Very well," agreed the boy.

Then he killed himself and, standing upright, presented his head and the sword with both hands to the stranger.

"I shall not let you down," said the stranger.

Then the boy's body fell.

The stranger took the head to the king, who was very pleased.

"This is the head of a brave man," said the stranger. "You should boil it in a seething cauldron."

The king did as he said. But even after three days and three nights the head would not melt away. It leapt out of the boiling water and glared in anger.

"This boy's head will not melt away," said the stranger, "unless Your Majesty comes to look at it."

Then the king walked up, the stranger struck him with the sword, and the king's head fell into the boiling water. The stranger then cut off his own head, which fell into the water too, and all three heads melted and intermingled. So the flesh and the soup were divided into three portions, and buried in a place called the Grave of the Three Kings. This grave is in the county of Beiyichun in the principality of Runan.

The King of Wu's Daughter

Fu Chai, the king of Wu, had a gifted and beautiful daughter of eighteen named Yu. She was in love with a learned youth of nineteen named Han Zhong. They exchanged secret messages and she promised to marry him. When Han went to study in the north, he asked his parents to arrange the marriage for him. But the king was angry and refused. Then the princess died of a broken heart and was buried outside the west gate.

Three years later Han returned and questioned his parents.

"The king was very angry and the princess died of a broken

heart," they told him. "Now she is in her grave."

At that Han wept bitterly and prepared a sacrifice to mourn for her. Then the princess appeared from her grave and shedding tears said:

"After you left you asked your parents to approach my father, and we thought our wish would surely come true, but fate was against us — alas!"

With a sidelong glance, she hung her head and sang:

> Crows were on the southern hill,
> Nets upon the north were spread;
> But the nets were set in vain,
> Far away the birds have fled.
> Fain would I have followed you,
> But detractors barred the way.
> Falling ill of grief, I died;
> Under yellow earth I lay.
> This was my unhappy fate,
> Doomed to weep day after day.
> Phoenix is the chief and queen
> Which each feathered fowl reveres;
> Phoenix, when it lost its mate,
> Wept and mourned for three whole years.
> Phoenix could not find a mate
> Though bright songsters filled the skies,
> So despite my humble looks,
> I appear before your eyes;
> And, though torn so far apart,
> Still you keep me in your heart!

After this song she wept and cried, unable to control her grief, and begged Han to accompany her into the grave.

"The dead and the living must go different ways," said Han. "I fear this would not be proper. I had better not."

"I know the dead and the living go different ways," she replied. "But once we part we shall never meet again. Are you afraid that because I am a ghost I will harm you? I am asking you in all sincerity — why don't you trust me?"

Touched by her words, Han saw her back. In the grave they feasted for three days and three nights, and completed the rites of marriage. When he was leaving she gave him a pearl one inch across.

"My reputation was spoilt and my wish never came true," she sighed. "What more is there to say? Take good care of yourself, and if you pass our house give my regards to the king."

When Han left the grave he went to the king and told him what had happened. Fu Chai flew into a rage.

"My daughter is dead!" he exclaimed. "This fellow is lying to dishonour the dead! He is simply a grave-robber who has stolen this pearl and trumped up this story of a ghost. Arrest him at once!"

But the young man escaped and went back to the grave where he told the princess what had happened.

"Don't worry," she said. "I shall go to speak to the king."

Then she went to see her father, who was dressing. At the sight of her he was overcome with joy, sorrow and surprise.

"What has brought you back to life?" he demanded.

"When the young scholar Han Zhong asked for my hand, you

refused him," she replied, kneeling. "I had lost my good name and broken my word, so I died. Recently he came back from far away, and hearing that I was dead prepared a sacrifice to mourn at my grave. I was so touched by his loyalty that I appeared to him and gave him that pearl. He is no grave-robber. Please do not punish him."

When the queen heard this she came out to embrace her child, and the princess vanished like a wisp of smoke.

Married to a Ghost

Lu Chong was a native of the principality of Fanyang. Thirty *li* to the west of his house was the graveyard of the Cui family, one of whom had held office as imperial custodian. The day before the winter solstice when Lu was twenty, he went out in a westerly direction to hunt. He sighted a deer and struck it with an arrow so that it fell, but it struggled up again. Then Lu gave chase and pursued it for a long way. Suddenly, a few hundred yards ahead of him to the north, he saw a large, tiled mansion like a government office. The deer had disappeared. The guard at the gate called out at his approach.

"Whose house is this?" asked Lu.

"The house of the imperial custodian."

"I am too shabby to call on him," said Lu.

Then someone came out with an armful of new clothes.

"Our master presents you with these," he announced.

Thereupon Lu changed his clothes and went in to see the imperial custodian, to whom he introduced himself. After they had drunk and eaten several courses, his host said to Lu:

"Your father recently honoured our humble house by sending a letter to ask for my daughter's hand for you. This is why I invited you in."

He showed Lu the letter. And though Lu had been a child when his father died, he could recognize the writing. With tears he consented. Then the imperial custodian sent a message to the inner chambers that Lu Chong had arrived and his daughter should dress for her wedding. He bade Lu go to the east chamber. By dusk word came from within that the girl was ready. When Lu entered the east chamber, she had alighted from her carriage. They stood on the carpet and bowed together, after which Lu stayed the customary three days. Then Cui said to him:

"You may go home now. I fancy my daughter has conceived. If she gives birth to a son, rest assured we will send him to you. If to a daughter, we will keep her ourselves."

He ordered his men to harness the carriage for Lu, who took his leave and went out. The imperial custodian saw him to the middle gate where they shook hands and shed tears. Outside the gate, Lu saw a cart drawn by oxen with a driver in blue, and found the clothes he had worn before and his bow and arrows. Then a man was sent out with a suit of clothes, which he gave to Lu with this message from his master: "We have just become related by marriage, and are very sorry that you are leaving so soon. Please accept this suit of clothes and set of bedding."

Lu mounted the cart which travelled as swiftly as lightning, and in no time he was home. When his people saw him, they did not know whether to be glad or sorry. Knowing that Cui was dead and that Lu had been in a grave, they felt rather uneasy.

Four years later, on the third day of the third month, Lu was strolling by the stream when he saw two carts drawn by oxen approach through the water. As they neared the bank, all those who were with him saw them. Lu opened the door at the back of the first cart and found Cui's daughter with a three-year-old boy. He was overjoyed to see her, and wanted to take her hand. But she raised her hand to point at the cart behind.

"You had better see my father," she said.

So he met the imperial custodian and greeted him. The girl gave the baby to Lu, and presented him with a golden bowl and a poem which read as follows:

> Glorious the sacred herb,
> So beautiful and bright,
> Its splendour appears at the appointed hour,
> And it is strange and rare;
> But before its blossoming time
> The summer frost withers it
> And blights its splendour for ever,
> So that it is lost to this world.
> Who can know the will of Heaven?
> Suddenly a wise man comes,
> The meeting is short and the departure soon,
> For all is ordained by the gods.
> What gift can I give my beloved?
> The golden bowl is for my son,
> And I bid an eternal farewell,
> Quite broken-hearted!

As soon as Lu took the child, the bowl and the poem, the two carts disappeared. When he carried the small boy home, everyone feared it must be a ghost and spat at it from a distance, but the child remained unchanged.

"Who is your father?" they asked.

It ran straight into Lu's arms.

At first all were amazed and felt forebodings, but then they read the poem and knew there was much mysterious traffic between the living and the dead.

Later Lu drove a cart to the market to sell the bowl. He asked a very high price, for he did not want to sell it so much as to find someone to identify it. An old woman slave recognized it, and went to tell her mistress:

"In the market I saw a man in a cart selling that bowl which was in Miss Cui's coffin."

Her mistress was the girl's aunt. She sent her son to look at the bowl, and when he found that what the slave said was true he went to Lu's cart and introduced himself.

"Formerly my aunt married the imperial custodian and had a daughter," he said. "The girl died before her marriage, and my mother in her grief presented a golden bowl to put in the coffin. Can you tell me how you came by this bowl?"

Lu told him the story, and the young man was moved. He took the bowl back to his mother, who asked to see the dead girl's son. All the Cui clansmen assembled, and when they found that the child looked like one of themselves yet resembled Lu as well, his case was proved.

"My niece was born at the end of the third month," said her

aunt. "Her father said, 'The spring is warm and we hope the infant will prosper, so let us name her Wenxiu (warm and prosperous).' The name sounded like 'wedded in the grave' — that was surely an omen."

The boy grew into a talented man, and became a provincial governor with a two-thousand-bushel salary. All his descendants to this day have been officials, while one — Lu Zhi — became famed throughout the empire.

Ji Kang and the Headless Ghost

Ji Kang was a man of noble character who liked to roam the country. Once travelling southwest of Luoyang, he came to a station named Huayang a few dozen *li* from the capital, where he put up for the night. There was no one else there that day — he was all alone. The station stood on an old execution ground, and accidents often happened to those who lodged there, but Ji Kang, who had a clear conscience, was not afraid. At about the first watch* he started strumming his lyre, playing several tunes. He was an excellent player, and a voice from the emptiness called: "Bravo!"

Ji Kang stopped playing and asked: "Who are you?"

"I am a dead man," answered the voice. "I have been here for thousands of years. When I heard you playing so sweetly and harmoniously on your lyre, I could not help coming over to lis-

---

* Eight or nine in the evening.

ten, as I used to love music too. Unfortunately I was killed unjustly and my body is mutilated, so I am not fit to be seen. But I greatly admire your playing and would like to watch you if you have no objection. Do play some more."

Ji Kang, having played again, beat his lyre with his hand and exclaimed: "It is growing late. Why don't you show yourself? Why should we care about appearances?"

Then the ghost appeared holding its head in its hand.

"After hearing you play, my heart feels light," it said. "I seem to have come to life again."

So they discussed their common interest in music, and the ghost spoke most lucidly and eloquently. Finally it asked Ji Kang: "May I borrow your lyre?"

Then Ji Kang let it play. Some of the tunes it played were common enough, but one piece called *Guangling San* was quite superb. Ji Kang learned this from the ghost, memorizing the whole of it within a few hours — a better melody than he had ever learned before. The ghost made him swear not to teach it to others and not to disclose the ghost's name. When dawn was about to break it said to Ji Kang:

"Although we met only this night, we have formed a thousand years' friendship. The long night is over — I must reluctantly leave you!"

The Two Hunters

One day Yuan Xiang and Gen Shuo of Yanxian in the principality of Kuaiji went out hunting. After crossing many hills and ridges, they saw six or seven wild goats ahead, and gave chase. The goats crossed an extremely narrow and steep stone bridge, and the hunters followed. Then they scaled a sheer red precipice, which was called the Red Wall Mountain. Water cascaded down it like a length of white cloth, and there was a cave in the mountain like an entrance. Entering this, they found a great plain within, where all the herbs and trees were sweetly scented. They discovered a hut in which two girls of about sixteen stayed. They were very beautiful and wore blue clothes. The name of one was Glistening Pearl, that of the other was... The girls were pleased to see the hunters.

"We have been looking forward to seeing you for a long time," they said.

So they became husbands and wives.

One day the two girls went out.

"One of our friends has found a husband," they said, "and we want to congratulate her."

Their sandals tinkled as they went over the precipice. The two hunters, who were homesick, quietly slipped away; but the girls came back in time to discover them. They agreed to let the men leave, and gave them a pouch which they told them never to open. So the hunters went home.

One day some time after, when they were out, some of their household opened the pouch. It was like a lotus with layer upon layer of petals, and after they reached the fifth layer a small blue bird flew out. When the men came back and learned what had happened, it was too late to regret. After this, as they were out ploughing and their family sent them the noonday meal as usual, they were found lying motionless in the fields. When their relatives went up to look, they found they were only shells — like the skins shed by cicadas.

The Lady of the White Stream

During the reign of Emperor An of the Jin Dynasty there was a young man in the county of Houguan named Xie Duan, who had lost his parents when a child and had no kinsmen. He was brought up by a neighbour. By the time he was eighteen, Xie was a modest, decent fellow who would do nothing unlawful. He had just begun to keep house for himself, but had not yet married. All his neighbours were concerned for him and wanted to find him a wife, but had so far not succeeded.

Every day Xie retired late and rose early, working hard in the fields from dawn till dusk. One day near his hamlet he found a large snail as big as a three-pint pot, which he took home as a curiosity and kept in a jar for a couple of weeks. Then each time he went home from the fields he would find hot food and drinks and the fire ready lit. Thinking his kind neighbour must have done this for him, after a few days he went over to thank him.

"That was not my work," said his neighbour. "You have no call to thank me."

Xie thought the good man had not understood him, so after the same thing had happened many times he questioned him again. The neighbour laughed and said:

"I know you have secretly taken a wife, and she is cooking for you. Why say it is my doing?"

Xie was quite dumbfounded, and could not understand this. One day he left home at cockcrow but came stealthily back during the morning and peeped through the fence. Then he saw a young girl come out of the jar and start lighting the fire in the kitchen. Upon going in to look for the snail in the jar, he realized it had changed into the girl. He walked into the kitchen.

"Where did you come from, young wife?" he asked. "And why are you cooking for me?"

The girl was most put out and tried to go back into the jar, but could not.

"I am the lady of the White Stream in the Milky Way," she told him. "The Heavenly Emperor took pity on you because you were all alone and lived such a virtuous life, so he told me to keep house for you for a time. In less than ten years you will become rich and find a wife, and then I should have left you. But now that you have surprised me for no reason, and seen my true form, I cannot stay here. I must leave you. You will do better though, from now on, if you work hard on the land and make extra money by fishing and cutting wood. I shall also leave you this shell. If you use it as a grain container, you will never find it empty."

He entreated her to stay, but she refused. There was a sudden storm and off she flew.

Then Xie set up a shrine and sacrificed to this goddess at festivals, and though not very rich he had enough. Later his neighbours found him a wife, and he became a magistrate. The Temple to the White Lady is now at the roadside.

The Tiantai Mountain Stream

In the fifth year of Yongping* in the reign of Emperor Ming of the Han Dynasty, Liu Chen and Ruan Zhao of Yanxian went to Tiantai Mountain to collect husks, but lost their way and could not find the road home. After thirteen days their rations were exhausted and they were dying of hunger, when they saw in the distance on the mountain a peach tree laden with fruit. Though it stood on a precipice over a fearful chasm and there was no path, they pulled themselves up by the creepers till they reached the top. After eating several peaches, their hunger abated and their strength returned. Coming down again, they filled their cups with water and were about to wash when they saw some fresh turnip leaves floating down from the gully. Then a wooden cup floated out with cooked sesame in it.

"There must be men living near by," they said.

So they swam upstream for two or three *li*, until they passed the mountain and came to a large stream.

By the stream were two divinely beautiful girls. They smiled when they saw the men coming with the cup.

---

* AD 62.

"Mr Liu and Mr Ruan have brought back our lost cup," they said.

Liu and Ruan had never met these girls before, but since the latter called them by their names as if they were old friends, they greeted them cheerfully in return.

"Why have you been so long?" asked the girls.

They invited the two men to their home, which was a house with bamboo tiles. By the south and east walls stood two great couches hung with red silk curtains, and the curtains had bells attached to each corner and were woven with gold and silver. Waiting by each couch were some dozen maid-servants, to whom the girls gave this order:

"Mr Liu and Mr Ruan have been travelling in the hills. Though they had peaches to eat, they are still exhausted. Prepare a meal as quickly as you can."

Then they had cooked sesame, cured goat meat and beef, all of which tasted delicious. Wine was served after the food. Then a number of girls came in, each carrying several peaches.

"Congratulations on the bridegrooms' arrival!" they said, laughing.

During the drinking, music was performed. Liu and Ruan were both frightened and pleased. At dusk they were led to the couches, and the two girls came to them. Their sweet, tender voices made the men forget their sorrow.

After ten days when they wished to go home, the girls said: "It was your good fortune to come here. Why should you want to leave?"

So they stayed on for six months. Then it was spring when the burgeoning flowers and trees and the chirping birds made them long for home, so they begged to be allowed to go.

"Your sins are drawing you away," said the girls. "What can we do?"

They summoned the other girls, thirty or forty in all, and after a feast with music they saw the two men off, showing them their homeward way.

When Liu and Ruan reached home, they found all their kinsmen and friends had died, the houses looked changed, and there was no one they knew. By dint of inquiries they found a descendant seven generations after them, who said that he had heard they had lost their way in the mountains and never returned.

In the eighth year of Taiyuan* of the Jin Dynasty, they left again and no one knows where they went.

The Dog as Go-Between

During the Han Dynasty, Huang Yuan of the principality of Taishan was opening his gate one morning when he saw a black dog sitting outside keeping watch, as if it belonged to the house. Huang fastened a string to the dog and took it out on a hunt with some neighbouring lads. When evening approached and he saw a deer, he let loose the dog, which ran so fast that try as he might he could not catch up with it. After following it for several *li*, he reached a mountain cave. He went in and about a hundred yards further on came to a highway flanked with ash and willow

---

* AD 383.

trees, with walls on either side. Then Huang followed the dog through a gate. He found several dozen rooms within, filled with beautiful girls who were splendidly attired, strumming lyres, plucking harps, or playing draughts.

When he reached the north pavilion, he found three rooms with two maids in attendance. Upon seeing Huang, they looked at each other and smiled.

"This is the husband the dog has brought for Miao Yin," they said.

One maid stayed there while the other went inside. Soon four maids came out and announced that Madame Tai Zhen had this proposal for Mr Huang:

"I have a daughter who has reached the marriageable age of fifteen, and fate has destined her to be your wife."

When night fell Huang was led inside to a hall facing south, with a lake in front of it. There was a pavilion in the lake, with entrances at the four corners. It was brightly lit and had curtains and couch inside. Miao Yin was a ravishing beauty, and her maids were pretty girls too. After the wedding was over, they feasted and went to bed. A few days later Huang wanted to go home, to announce his marriage to his family.

"Mortal and immortal are different," said Miao Yin. "We cannot stay long together after all."

The next day she took off her jade pendant as a parting gift for him, and shed tears by the steps.

"We cannot remain together," she said, "but my love for you is deep. Think of me on the first of each third month, and fast and purify yourself on that day."

The four maids saw Huang out, and in half a day he reached

home. He longed for his fairy wife, and each year at the appointed time he caught a glimpse of her carriage gliding through the air.

The Powder Girl

A very rich family had an only son, to whom they were devoted. At the market one day he saw a beautiful girl selling powder made of white lead. He fell in love with her, but with no one to introduce him he had to make buying powder his pretext to go there. He went to her stall every day, and left without a word after making his purchase. After some time the girl became suspicious. Next time he turned up she asked him:

"What do you need all that powder for?"

He told her that he loved her but had not dared introduce himself, that because he longed to see her he had used this pretext. The girl was very touched, and they agreed to meet the next evening.

That night the young man lay in his room waiting for her; and at dusk, sure enough, she came. He was in raptures. Embracing her, he said:

"Now my wish is granted!"

Then in his ecstasy he died.

The girl was terrified and did not know what to do. She ran back to the powder shop. When it was time for breakfast, the lad's parents were surprised that he did not appear, and upon going to look they found him dead.

Before burying him they opened his cases and discovered over a hundred packets of powder, large and small, heaped there.

"It must be this powder that killed my son," said his mother.

She went to the market to buy powder from all the shops, and when she reached the girl's stall she found the same packaging. Then she laid hold of her and said:

"Why did you kill my son?"

At this the girl burst out crying and told the truth. The young man's parents did not believe her, though, and haled her to the court to accuse her of murder.

"I am not afraid to die," she said, "but let me see him once more and mourn over him."

The magistrate agreed.

She clasped the lad's body and wept bitterly.

"Alas that we should come to this!" she sighed. "But if there is a spirit after death, I shall die content."

All of a sudden the young man came back to life, and told what had passed. They became husband and wife and had many descendants.

The Magistrate and the Local Deity

Zhen Chong, a native of Zhongshan, was appointed magistrate of Yunshe. On his way to his post he had to pass the county of Huihuai, where he was informed that the son of the local deity wished to call on him. Soon the deity's son arrived, young and handsome. They exchanged the usual courtesies.

"My father sent me here," said the young god, "because he wants to be allied to your noble house, and hopes you will take my younger sister in marriage. I have come to bring you this message."

"I am past my prime and have a wife already." Zhen was taken aback. "How can I do such a thing?"

"My sister is young and remarkably beautiful. We must find a good match for her. How can you refuse?"

"I am an old man and I have a wife. It would not be right."

They argued back and forth several times, but Zhen was adamant. The young god looked annoyed.

"Then my father will come himself," he said. "I doubt if you can refuse him."

He left, followed by a large retinue of attendants with caps and whips on both banks of the river.

Soon the local deity arrived in person with an equipage like a baron's. His carriage had a dark green canopy and red reins, and was escorted by several chariots. His daughter rode in an open carriage with several dozen silk pennants and eight maids before it, dressed in embroidered gowns more splendid than mortal eye has ever seen. They pitched a tent on the bank near Zhen and spread a carpet, after which the local deity alighted and sat by the low table on a white woollen rug. He had a jade spittoon, a handkerchief box of tortoise-shell and a white fly-whisk. His daughter remained on the east bank, with eunuchs carrying whisks at her side and maids in front. The local deity then ordered his assistant officers — some sixty of them — to sit before him, and called for music. The instruments they used seemed to be of glass.

"I have a humble daughter dear to my heart," said the god. "Since you come of a virtuous and renowned family, we are eager to be connected with you by marriage. That is why I sent my son with this request."

"I am old and decrepit," replied Zhen Chong. "I already have a wife and my son is quite big. So although I am tempted by this proffered honour, I must beg to decline."

"My daughter is twenty," continued the deity. "She is beautiful and gentle, and possessed of all the virtues. As she is now on the bank, there is no need for any preparation: the wedding can take place at once."

Zhen Chong stood out stubbornly, calling the god an evil spirit. He drew his sword and laid it on his knees, determined to resist to the death, and refused to discuss the matter any further. The local deity flew into a passion. He summoned three leopards and two tigers, which opened their red mouths wide and shook the earth with their roars as they leapt at Zhen. They attacked several dozen times, but Zhen held them at bay till dawn when the god withdrew, thwarted. He left behind one carriage and several dozen men to wait for Zhen, however. Then Zhen moved into the Huihuai County office. The waiting carriage and men followed him in, and a man in plain dress and cap bowed to him and advised him to stay there and not go any further.

Zhen Chong did not dare leave until after ten days. Even then a man in a cap with a whip still followed him home. And he had not been home many days before his wife contracted an illness and died.

The Lovelorn Spirit

Pang E of the principality of Julu was a very handsome man. A daughter of the Shi family in that district fell in love with him at first sight, and when later she was seen calling on him his wife grew extremely jealous. One day, hearing the girl coming, she bade her maids tie her up and take her home; but on the way the young lady vanished like smoke. When the maids reported this to her family, the girl's father was astounded.

"My daughter has not left the house," he said. "How dare you slander us like this?"

But Pang's father watched his son carefully, and discovered the girl in his study one night. He seized her himself and went to the Shi family. When the girl's father saw her, he was amazed.

"I have just come from the inner rooms," he said. "I saw my daughter there working with her mother. How can she be here?"

He told his servants to call his daughter out, and the moment the real girl appeared the other vanished. The puzzled father told his wife to investigate, and the girl explained that after peeping at Pang E once when he was in their hall she had dreamed ever since of going to his home, and had been caught by his wife when she went in.

"Well, I never!" exclaimed her father. "When a spirit is deeply moved, it can assume any form it chooses. So what vanished was your spirit after all!"

The girl resolved not to marry anyone else. A year later, however, Pang's wife contracted a strange disease which proved incurable. Then Pang sent betrothal gifts to the Shi family and married their daughter.

The Cedar Pillow

The priest of Jiaohu Temple had a cedar pillow, which was in his possession for more than thirty years and had a small crack at the back. When Tang Lin of this county was travelling on business, he passed the temple and prayed for good fortune there. The priest asked if he was married, and told him to go into the hole in the pillow. He did so, and found vermilion gates, marble palaces and towers, more magnificent than any to be seen on earth. There he met Marshal Zhao who found him a wife, by whom he had six children — four boys and two girls. Then he was recommended for the post of imperial librarian and promoted to the rank of imperial secretary. So he lived in the pillow with no thought of his home, until at last things went ill for him. Then the priest called him out, and he emerged. Though many years had passed within the pillow, only a short time had elapsed outside.

The New Ghost

A new ghost, who was very thin and haggard, came across an old friend of his dead for about twenty years, who looked fat and sleek. They greeted each other.

"How are you?" asked his friend.

"I am so hungry I cannot stand it," he said. "You must know all the tricks. Please tell me what to do."

"That's easy," said his friend. "So long as you work wonders men will be frightened, then they will give you food."

The new ghost went to the east side of the village, where he found a family of zealous Buddhists. There was a mill to the west of the house and the ghost started turning this mill as if he were a man. Then the master of the house said to his children:

"Buddha has taken pity on our poverty and sent this ghost to turn the mill for us."

He brought up cartloads of wheat, until by night the ghost had ground dozens of bushels and had to leave, exhausted.

"You cheated me!" he swore at his friend.

"Try again," said his friend. "You'll get food."

Then he went to the west side of the village to a family of zealous Taoists. There was a mortar by the gate, and the ghost started pounding the pestle as if he were a man.

"Yesterday this ghost went to help so-and-so," said the householder. "Today it has come to help me. Let us carry grain to it."

He bade the maids winnow the grain, and by evening the ghost was worn out but still he received no food. When he went back that night he was furious.

"We are relatives by marriage, not ordinary friends," he accused the other ghost. "Why should you cheat me? I have helped men for two whole days but not got one bowl of food."

"You have just been unlucky," replied his friend. "It is hard to make an impression on Buddhists and Taoists. If you go and work wonders in ordinary families, you are bound to be given food."

Then the new ghost went to a house which had a bamboo pole at the gate. Going in, he saw women eating by the window. There was a white dog in the courtyard, and the ghost picked it up so that it seemed to be walking in the air. When the family saw this they were amazed, and said they had never seen such a wonder before. They consulted a fortune-teller.

"You have a hungry visitor," he told them. "If you kill the dog and put it with sweetmeats, wine and rice in the courtyard as a sacrifice, all will be well."

They did this, and the ghost made a hearty meal. After that it always took its friend's advice, and went on working wonders.

The Scholar by the Roadside

When Xu Yan of Yangxian was travelling in the hills of Suian, he came across a scholar of about seventeen or eighteen. The young man, who was lying by the roadside, said that his feet ached and asked for a lift in the goose cage which Xu was carrying. Xu thought he was joking. But the scholar got into the cage, which looked no larger than before while the scholar looked no smaller. He sat down quietly beside the two geese, and they did not seem to mind him. Xu carried the cage again, but did not find it any heavier.

Further on, when he stopped to rest under a tree, the scholar came out of the cage and offered to treat him to a meal. Xu accepted with pleasure, and the scholar took from his mouth a copper tray laid with all manner of delicacies. The utensils were of copper, and the food had a rare taste and fragrance. After several cups of wine, the scholar said to Xu:

"I have a girl with me. May I ask her to join us?"

"Certainly," replied Xu.

Then from his mouth the scholar produced a girl of fifteen or sixteen, richly dressed and of surpassing beauty. She sat down and feasted with them. Presently the scholar was tipsy and went to lie down.

"Though I have married this man," said the girl to Xu, "I really hate him. I have brought another man with me. Now that my husband is asleep, I shall call him out. Please don't say anything."

"Certainly not," agreed Xu.

Then the girl produced from her mouth another young man of twenty-three or four, who looked intelligent and charming, and who began chatting with Xu. Just then the scholar started to wake up, and the girl took a silk screen from her mouth to hide the new man. The scholar made the girl join him.

The newcomer then told Xu: "Though that girl is fond of me, I don't care for her. I have brought another girl with me and would like to see her now. Please don't let her know."

"Very well," agreed Xu.

Then the second man took from his mouth a girl of twenty or thereabouts. They feasted and amused themselves for some time, till they heard the scholar stirring.

"Those two are getting up," said the second man.

Then he put the girl back into his mouth.

The first girl returned and told Xu: "The scholar is getting up."

She swallowed her friend, and sat alone with Xu.

Then the scholar came out and told him: "I am sorry I slept so long. You must have been bored sitting all by yourself. It is getting late now, so I will say goodbye."

At that he swallowed the girl as well as the utensils, leaving only the big copper tray for Xu. This tray was some two feet across, and in parting the scholar said:

"I have nothing worth giving, but keep this as a souvenir."

During the Taiyuan period Xu was an adviser of the Imperial Library and showed the tray to Minister Zhang San, who discovered from the inscription that it was made in the third year of Yongping. *

The Fairy of Qingxi Temple

When Zhao Wenshao of Kuaiji was the crown prince's steward, he lived near Central Bridge at Qingxi, in the next alley to Minister Wang Shuqing's house about two hundred paces away. One autumn night a splendid moon made him feel homesick, and leaning on his gate he sang the sad song *The Crows Fly West*. Then a maid of about sixteen in blue clothes came up to him and said:

"Greetings from my young mistress in the Wang family. She heard you sing while we were playing in the moonlight, and sends her regards to you."

As it was still early and not everyone had gone to bed, Zhao was not unduly surprised. He answered politely, and invited the young lady over.

---

* AD 60.

In a short time she came. She seemed eighteen or nineteen, her gait and air were sweet, and she had two maids with her. When Zhao asked where she lived, she pointed at the minister's house.

"Over there," she said. "When I heard you sing, I decided to call. Will you sing a song for me?"

Then Zhao sang *Grass Grows on the Rock*. He had a clear and melodious voice, and she enjoyed the words too.

"If you have a pitcher," she said, "you need not be afraid of having no water." She turned to her maids and told them: "Go back and fetch my cithern, and I shall play to the gentleman."

Presently the cithern was brought, and she played two or three haunting and plaintive airs. Then she bade her maids sing *Heavy Frost*, loosening her belt to fasten the cithern to her waist and play an accompaniment. The song was this:

> Dusk falls, a cold wind blows,
> Dead leaves cling to the bough,
> Alas, you cannot know
> The love my heart holds now!
> The curtain of my bed
> Is white with heavy frost;
> The frost is falling still,
> And I alone am lost.

After this song it was late and she spent the night with him, departing at the fourth watch just before dawn, and leaving him her gold hairpin as a keepsake. In return Zhao gave her a silver bowl and a white glass spoon.

When day broke Zhao went out and happened to pass the temple. Going in to rest by the shrine, he was surprised to find the bowl there, while behind the screen he discovered the glass spoon. The cithern still had a belt attached to it. In the temple stood the image of the fairy, with maids in blue dress in front — all those he had seen the night before. This took place in the fifth year of Yuanjia.[*] But nothing like this ever happened to him again.

The Lost Sutra

Ding Cheng, a native of the principality of Jiyin, became magistrate of Ningyin during the Jianyuan period.[**]

One day a woman in the north suburb went to draw water from a well outside, when a man who looked like a foreigner with long nose and deep-set eyes passed by and asked for a drink. After drinking the stranger vanished, while the woman was seized with a pain in the belly which grew worse and worse. After groaning for some time she abruptly sat up and gave orders in a foreign tongue. Several dozen neighbouring families came to watch. The woman asked for pen and paper, and being given a pen started writing in some foreign language — spidery words that ran from side to side.[***] She covered five sheets of paper which she tossed to the ground, but when she ordered people to read them, no one

---

[*] AD 428.

[**] AD 343-344.

[***] Unlike Chinese which was written vertically.

in that district could decipher them. She pointed at a small boy of about ten and said that he could read it, and sure enough the boy took the papers and read them. The spectators were amazed and completely bewildered. Then the woman told the boy to dance, and he stood up, raising his legs and gesturing with his hands. They danced and sang together for a while.

This was reported to Magistrate Ding Cheng, who summoned the woman and boy, but she told him she had not known what she was doing. Anxious to find out what the writing was, the magistrate sent an officer with it to the Xuchang Monastery where one old inmate was a foreign monk. This foreigner was astounded.

"Part of a Buddhist sutra was lost," he told them. "As we would have had to travel far to find the original, we were afraid we should never get the whole text. Some parts we could recite, but not all, and this was the missing portion."

It was copied out and kept in the monastery.

Iron Mortar

During the Song period there was a native of Donghai named Xu, whose wife died after bearing him a son named Iron Mortar. Then he married a daughter of the Chen family, but she was a cruel woman who determined to kill her stepson. She bore a son herself, and at his birth she swore:

"If you don't kill Iron Mortar, you are no son of mine."

So she named her own boy Iron Pestle, hoping the pestle would overcome the mortar. She kept thrashing her stepson and treating him cruelly, giving him no food when he was hungry and no padded clothes when he was cold. Xu was a coward, and besides he was often away, so the stepmother could do just as she pleased. And finally Iron Mortar died — of hunger, cold and beatings. He was then only sixteen.

About ten days after his death his ghost came back and went to his stepmother's bed.

"I am Iron Mortar," it said. "I did no one any wrong, yet I was cruelly murdered. My mother lodged a complaint in heaven, and now I have an order from heaven to fetch Iron Pestle. He will suffer as I did and leave this earth very soon. I shall wait for him here."

The voice was like Iron Mortar's when he was alive, and though the household and the guests could not see him they could all hear him. And the ghost took up its quarters on the beam.

Xu's wife kneeled to apologize, slapped her own face and sacrificed to the ghost.

"That is no use," said the ghost. "You starved me to death — how can you make up for that with a meal now?"

At night she secretly complained.

"How dare you complain of me?" asked the ghost angrily. "I shall break your roof."

They heard the sound of a saw, and sawdust fell. Then there came a great crash as if the beam had collapsed. The whole household rushed outside, but when they lighted a torch to see the damage, nothing at all had happened.

Then the ghost swore at its stepbrother: "After killing me, why should you live here in comfort? I shall burn your house down."

At that they saw a fire with much smoke and flames, and the whole household was alarmed; but presently the fire died down of itself, and the thatched roof was left undamaged. The ghost used to abuse them like this every day, after which it would burst into song:

> Oh, peach blossom and prune blossom,
> What if the frost should cover you?
> Oh, ripe peaches and ripe prunes,
> One frost and all's over with you!

The air was a very sad one, as if the ghost was lamenting its early death. Its six-year-old stepbrother had been ill ever since the ghost came. His whole body ached, his belly became swollen and full of gas, and he could not eat. The ghost kept beating him too, and wherever it beat him the boy turned black and blue. After a month the child died, and the ghost disappeared for good.

The Merchant's Revenge

When Emperor Wu of the Liang Dynasty wanted to build a monastery at his father's tomb, he could not find good enough timber, and all the authorities were ordered to make a search.

A rich man of Chu'a named Hong gathered together much merchandise with his relatives, and went to Xiangzhou to do business. About a year later he acquired a wooden raft some thousand yards long, of a magnificent and very rare wood. On his return to Nanjing, the local official Meng Shaoqing was so eager to please the authorities that he heaped accusations on Hong. Because he had clothing and silk left unsold, he was accused of stealing these during his journey. He was also charged with having more splendid possessions than any merchant should own. So Meng condemned him to death, and confiscated his raft for the monastery. He obtained government sanction for the execution.

On the day of his execution, Hong told his wife and children to put yellow paper, pen and ink in his coffin, saying that if he retained consciousness after death he would take revenge. He wrote down Meng's name several dozen times and swallowed the paper with the names on it.

A month later, as Meng was sitting in his office, he saw Hong coming towards him. At first he tried to evade and resist him, then he admitted his guilt but begged for mercy, and finally he vomited blood and died. All the gaolers and clerks involved in this case died one after the other, so that in less than a year they had all perished.

The monastery was no sooner built than fire from the sky destroyed it, leaving nothing at all. Even the bases of the wooden pillars, which were set deep under the earth, were reduced to ashes.

Translated by Yang Xianyi
and Gladys Yang

Selections from "New Anecdotes of Social Talk"

THESE anecdotes record the sayings, noble and eccentric deeds and idiosyncrasies of famous men from the Eastern Han to the Eastern Jin dynasties (AD 25-420) and are probably the work of Prince Liu Yiqing of the Song Dynasty. A native of Jingkou, now Zhenjiang in Jiangsu, and the second son of Prince Jing of Changsha, he was invested Prince of Linchuan and held many high offices. A retiring man of literary tastes, his works also include *Records of Light and Darkness*, though since history records that he was a patron of writers rather than a gifted writer himself it is possible that the work is a compilation by many hands.

Anecdotes Concerning Cao Cao

When Cao Cao was young he often went out with Yuan Shao in search of adventure. Once they saw a wedding in progress, and crept into the bridegroom's courtyard. At night they shouted: "Thief! Thief!" When everyone rushed out from the bridal chamber to catch the thief, Cao Cao went in with his sword to kidnap the bride, and then made off with Yuan Shao. They lost their way and Yuan Shao fell among brambles and could not get out. Then Cao Cao cried:

"Here's the thief!"

Yuan Shao leaped with fright, and so they managed to escape.

*

When Yuan Shao was a youth, he sent a man at night to throw a dagger at Cao Cao. The dagger was aimed too low and hit the couch. Guessing that the next throw would be aimed high, Cao Cao lay as flat as he could, and the second attempt failed too.

*

Cao Cao once said: "No one must come near me when I am asleep. If anyone does, I will cut him down with my sword in my sleep. Let all my followers beware!"

Later he pretended to be asleep, and when one of his favourite ladies tiptoed up to cover him with a quilt, he cut her down and killed her. After that whenever he slept no one dared go near.

*

In one of his campaigns Cao Cao failed to find a watering place, and all his troops were suffering from thirst. Then he announced that there was a great plum orchard ahead, the trees laden with sweet and sour fruit which could quench thirst. Hearing this his men's mouths watered and they managed to struggle on to their destination.

*

Cao Cao claimed that he always knew when anyone wanted to harm him. And he told one of his favourite followers:

"Come to me with a dagger on you. I will say I have a premonition of danger, and have you arrested to be killed. But just say nothing about this trick, and no harm will come to you. In fact I shall reward you well."

That fellow trusted him and had no misgivings. Then Cao Cao had him killed, and that man did not realize till his death that he had been deceived. All Cao Cao's followers thought his sense of danger was genuine, and conspirators were disheartened.

*

One day Cao Cao had to receive a Hunnish envoy. Afraid that he did not look distinguished enough to overawe this barbarian, he ordered Cui Yan to take his place while he stood by the couch holding the sword. After the audience he sent a spy to ask the envoy:

"What did you think of our prince?"

"Your prince is a striking figure," replied the envoy. "But the man with the sword by the couch is a true hero."

When Cao Cao heard this, he sent pursuers to capture and kill the Hun.

The Man Who Risked His Life for His Friend

Xun Jubo travelled a great distance to see a friend who was ill. The place was being attacked by the Huns when he went.

"I shall die here," said his friend. "You had better go."

"I came all this way to see you," retorted Xun. "And now you tell me to leave! How can I act against my conscience simply to save my skin?"

The invaders came and said to him: "At our great army's approach the whole district has fled. Who are you that dare to stay here?"

Xun replied: "My friend is ill and I cannot leave him. Let me beg you to take my life instead of his."

Then the Huns said: "We are wicked men coming to the land of the just."

They withdrew their troops and the whole district was spared.

The Coral Tree

Shi Chong and Wang Kai rivalled each other in extravagant display: their clothes and equipage were as magnificent as possible. Since the emperor was Wang Kai's nephew, he often assisted him. Once he gave him a coral tree over two feet high with many branches, the like of which Wang had never seen before.

Wang Kai showed this to Shi Chong, who took one look at it and then smashed it with an iron wand. Wang Kai grew heated over the loss of this treasure and disgusted at Shi's envious behaviour.

"Don't worry," said Shi Chong.

He told his attendants to fetch his coral trees. Six or seven of them were more than three feet high, with superb branches and a dazzling colour, while he had many more as good as that of Wang Kai.

Wang Kai felt considerably chastened.

Dongfang Shuo the Jester

Once the nurse of Emperor Wu of the Han Dynasty committed some offence outside the palace, and the emperor was about to punish her. She asked Dongfang Shuo to help her.

"This cannot be argued," said the jester. "But if you really hope to succeed, look at the emperor again and again as you are being led away. Don't say anything though. This is your only chance in a thousand."

When the nurse was brought in, Dongfang Shuo was also present.

"You are a fool," he said to her. "How could the emperor remember your former kindness? He was a child when you were nursing him."

The emperor, despite his ambition and ruthlessness, was a man of feeling. Moved with pity, he pardoned the nurse.

The Three Evils

When Zhou Chu was a young man, his savage temper and love of adventure made all his countrymen fear him. Havoc was caused in the district of Yixing by a serpent in the lake and a tiger in the mountain. So the local people spoke of their Three Evils, counting Zhou the worst of the three. Someone advised him to kill the tiger and the serpent, hoping in this way to get rid of two of the evils. First Zhou Chu killed the tiger, then he plunged into the lake to grapple with the serpent. The monster came to the surface and submerged again, swimming many *li*, but Zhou stayed close beside it. After three days and three nights the local people thought he must be dead, and were indeed congratulating themselves when Zhou came back after finally killing the serpent. When he heard men speaking joyfully of his death, he realized that he, too, was considered a pest and determined to mend his ways.

He went to the district of Wu to look for the Lu brothers.

Failing to find Lu Ji, he sought out Lu Yun and explained to him that he wanted to mend his ways, but after so many wasted years it seemed too late to change.

Lu Yun said: "The superior men of old thought it good to know the truth even if one had to die that very evening. And you are still in your prime. Moreover a man should worry if he has no ideal in life, not if he has no fame."

Then Zhou Chu corrected his faults, and became a loyal and pious man.

Wang Huizhi's Idiosyncrasies

Wang Huizhi once lodged for a short time in an empty house belonging to another man. He ordered bamboos to be planted there.

Someone asked: "Why take so much trouble when you are staying here for such a short time?"

Wang merely recited poetry for a while, then pointing at the bamboos asked:

"Can one live a single day without this gentleman?"

One night when Wang Huizhi was living in Shanyin there was a heavy fall of snow. Upon waking and opening his door he ordered wine to be served. He gazed around at the expanse of white, and strolled up and down reciting Zuo Si's poems on a hermit's life. Then he suddenly remembered Dai Kui, then in Yan County, and set out that same night in a small boat to visit him. The journey took one whole day; yet when he reached the door he turned back instead of entering.

Asked the reason, he said: "I set out on a happy impulse. Now that mood is over, I am going back. What need was there to see him?"

Liu Ling the Drunkard

One day Liu Ling had too much to drink, but feeling parched he asked his wife for more wine. She poured away the wine and broke the pitcher, and with tears in her eyes advised him against tippling.

"You are drinking too much — it is bad for your health. You must stop it!"

Liu Ling said: "Very well. But I cannot control myself. The only way is to swear before the gods to give it up. Prepare the sacrificial meat and wine."

His wife agreed to this.

She placed wine and meat before the shrine and asked Liu Ling to make his oath. Liu Ling knelt down and prayed:

"Heaven gave me life and made me famed for drinking. I drink ten pints at a sitting, and five will cure my headache afterwards. A man should not listen to the words of a woman."

Then he drained the wine and ate the meat, and soon was drunk again.

Wen Qiao's Second Marriage

Lord Wen Qiao was a widower. A distant aunt of his named Liu, whose family had suffered in the wars, had an only daughter — a pretty, intelligent girl. Her mother asked Wen Qiao to find her a husband, but he was eager to marry the girl himself.

"It is hard to find a good match," he demurred. "What would you say to some man like myself?"

His aunt replied: "After the trouble we have seen, all I want is enough to live on — that is all I hope for in my declining years. How can I aim so high?"

A few days later he told her: "I have found a man. His family is respectable and he is a noted official, no less well known than I."

He sent a jade mirror-stand as betrothal gift, and his aunt was overjoyed.

After the wedding ceremony, the girl pushed the fans aside, clapped her hands and laughed.

"I guessed it would be this old fellow. I suspected as much!"

The jade mirror-stand was a trophy presented to Wen Qiao when he served under Liu Kun in the northern expedition against Liu Cong.

The Lover Who Scaled a High Wall

Han Shou, Jia Chong's secretary, was a handsome man. One day when Jia Chong held a council, his daughter saw Han through the window and fell in love with him. She began to pine for him and to write love poems. Her maid went to Han Shou's house and told him this, dwelling on the remarkable beauty of her mistress till Han's interest was aroused. He begged the maid to take a secret message, making a tryst to visit the girl at night. And being very agile, he climbed over the wall into her house without her family's knowledge.

After this, Jia Chong observed that his daughter took a great interest in her appearance and seemed to be strangely elated. Later, during an assembly of all his officers, he detected a rare perfume about Han Shou's person. This perfume was part of the tribute from abroad: a single application retained its fragrance for months. And since the emperor had given this scent to Jia Chong and Chen Qian alone, no one else could have it. Accordingly Jia Chong began to suspect that Han Shou was having an affair with his daughter. But the house was surrounded by high walls, and the passages and doors were narrow. How could anyone get in? On the pretext that he had been robbed, he ordered workmen to repair the walls. They reported that every part was in good condition except the northeast corner, where there appeared to be footprints, though the wall was too high to climb. Then Jia Chong questioned his daughter's maids, and learned the truth from them. He kept it a secret, but married his daughter to Han.

Two Commentators

Fu Qian had made a careful study of the *Zhou Dynasty Annals* and was writing a commentary on this work, but wanted to compare notes with some other scholar. When he heard that Cui Lie was giving his students lectures on the subject he hired himself to Cui as a cook, not disclosing his real name. He listened to the lectures outside the door. And when he found that Cui's knowledge was no greater than his own, he started discussing certain points with the students. Cui had no idea who he was, but knowing Fu Qian's reputation he suspected that this was he. One day he went to him at dawn and called his name while he was still asleep. Taken by surprise, Fu answered. Then they became good friends.

A Talented Brigand

Dai Yuan was a wild young fellow who loved adventure. He turned brigand in the Huai River Valley and held up passing merchants. One day he ordered his young men to rob Lu Ji, who was travelling back to Luoyang on leave with considerable luggage. Dai sat on the bank on his couch to issue orders, directing the operation with great skill. And since he was outstandingly intelligent, even as a brigand he behaved with distinction.

"You are a man of great ability," called Lu Ji from his boat. "Why should you be a brigand?"

Then Dai Yuan was moved and threw away his sword to join Lu Ji on his boat. His original mind commanded the other's respect. They became sworn brothers and Lu Ji recommended him to the court. After the imperial house of Jin moved south of the Yangtse River, Dai Yuan was appointed a general.

A Wife's Advice

When Xu Yun of the Wei Dynasty was in the Ministry of Civil Affairs, he employed so many men from his own district that Emperor Ming sent guards to have him arrested. His wife gave him a warning.

"You may convince His Majesty by argument, but on no account plead for mercy!"

When he entered the imperial presence, the emperor questioned him.

Xu Yun replied: "A man should recommend only those whom he knows well. I know my fellow countrymen. Your Majesty can investigate to see if they discharge their duties competently or not. If they are not up to their work, I shall plead guilty."

Then the government investigated these men and found them competent. So Xu Yun was released. And since his clothes were torn and soiled, the emperor presented him with new.

When Xu Yun was arrested the whole of his household had wailed except his wife.

"There is no cause for alarm," she said calmly. "He will be back."

She made some broth against his return, and sure enough before long he came home.

The Soldier Who Loved Wine

During the revolt of Su Jun, the entire Yu family fled. Yu Bing, then governor of the district of Wu, was deserted by all his officers and men. He escaped alone with one of the district soldiers, who rowed him down the River Qiantang hidden under some matting in a little boat. As Su Jun had offered a reward for Yu Bing and his men, a strict search was in progress. The soldier moored by an island to go ashore for a drink. Coming back, drunk, he waved his oar at the boat.

"Who is looking for Governor Yu? I have him here!"

Yu Bing was horror-struck and dared not move. But when the officers in charge saw that the boat was too small to carry much and the soldier was completely drunk, they suspected nothing. They let the craft proceed to the River Zhe, where Yu Bing found refuge with the Wei family of Shanyin. In this way he escaped death.

The revolt once over, he decided to reward the soldier. He asked him what he wanted.

"I come from a humble family, so I want no rank or insignia," was the answer. "I have worked hard at low tasks since my boyhood, and often been sorry that I could not drink my fill. All I ask is wine to last me to the end of my days."

Then Yu Bing had a large house built for him, bought him

slaves, and saw to it that he had always a hundred pints of wine. So all men said that this soldier was not merely intelligent but knew how to live.

Translated by Yang Xianyi
and Gladys Yang

Record of Buddhist Countries

THE author of this book is the renowned Buddhist monk Fa Xian (AD 335-420), who was born at Wuyang in Pingyang, now Xiangyuan in Shanxi, and renounced the world while still a boy. Discovering many defects in the early Chinese translations of Buddhist sutras, he determined upon a journey to India in search of the originals. In AD 399 he struck west from Chang'an, now Xi'an in Shaanxi, crossed the Pamirs into Central Asia and eventually arrived in India, where he obtained many sutras and learned Sanskrit. He continued south to Sri Lanka and returned home by sea, landing in AD 412 at Qingzhou near the Laoshan Mountains in Shandong Province. The following year he arrived in Jiankang, the southern capital, now Nanjing, where he translated much of the Buddhist canon and wrote the *Record of Buddhist Countries*, setting down his experiences during more than a decade of travel through some 30 lands.

The present extract deals with central India and Sri Lanka.

The Lesser Snow Mountains and the Countries of Rohi, Bannu and Bhida

...After staying in Nagarahara for three months during the winter, Fa Xian and his two companions, Hui Jing and Dao Zheng, struck south across the Lesser Snow Mountains which are covered with snow in summer as well as winter. As they were climbing the northern side of the mountains, which has no sun, sudden icy blasts swept down and made them shiver. White foam began to issue from Hui Jing's mouth, and he could go no further.

"It is all up with me," he said to Fa Xian. "But you press on. Don't stay here to perish with me!"

And thereupon he died. Fa Xian caressed him, lamenting bitterly.

"You have failed in your purpose!" he cried. "Yet such is fate!"

They gathered their remaining strength to push forward again and, proceeding to the south side of the mountains, reached the country of Rohi. Here they found about 3,000 monks of both the Mahayana and Hinayana Schools. And here they stayed for the summer retirement. * The summer over, they descended into the valley to the south, and walked for ten days till they came to the country of Bannu. Here there are also about 3,000 monks, all of whom study Hinayana Buddhism.

---

* It was the Buddhist custom for the monks to remain in retirement during the summer or rainy season.

Journeying eastward for three days, they re-crossed the Indus River where the ground is smooth and level on both sides. Beyond the river lies the country called Bhida. Buddhism flourishes here and both the Mahayana and Hinayana Schools are studied. On seeing two monks from China, the people of that country were greatly moved.

"How is it that men from across the border will leave their homes for the sake of the Law and come so far to seek Buddhism?" they demanded.

They therefore provided them with all that they needed, and entertained them according to Buddhist customs.

The Country of Mathura

Travelling southeast for nearly eighty *yojanas*, [*] they passed a great number of monasteries with some ten thousand monks altogether. Having passed all these, they reached a country called Mathura where, once again, they crossed the Yamuna River. On the right and left sides of the river are twenty monasteries with some 3,000 monks. Buddhism flourishes there.

All the kings of the Indian countries west of the Desert of Lop are devout believers in Buddha's Law. When making offerings to monks they take off their crowns and, with the members of the royal house and their ministers, serve food to the monks with

---

[*] A *yojana* was regarded as a day's march for the army; but in Buddhist canons it is sometimes as little as five miles.

their own hands. This done, they spread a carpet on the ground and sit down on it in front of the principal monk. They dare not sit on couches in the presence of monks. The rules for this making of offerings by kings have been handed down from the time of Buddha till now.

The Climate and Customs of the Middle Kingdom

The region to the south is known as the Middle Kingdom. The climate is temperate without frost or snow. The people are rich and contented, unencumbered by any poll-tax or official restrictions. Only those who till the king's land pay a land tax, and they are free to go or stay as they please. The kings govern without recourse to capital punishment, but offenders are fined lightly or heavily according to the nature of their crime. Even those who plot high treason only have their right hands cut off. The king's attendants, guards and retainers all receive emoluments and pensions. The people of this country kill no living creatures, drink no wine, and eat no onion or garlic. The single exception to this is the Chandalas, who are known as "Evil Men" and are segregated from the others. When they enter towns or markets they strike a piece of wood to announce their presence, so that others may know they are coming and avoid them. Neither pigs nor fowl are kept in this country and no living creatures are sold. There are no butchers or wine-sellers in the markets. Shells are used as currency in trading. Only the Chandala hunters sell flesh.

After Buddha's Nirvana, the kings, elders and lay Buddhists built monasteries for the monks and provided them with houses, gardens and fields, with husbandmen and cattle to cultivate them. Title-deeds inscribed on iron were handed down from king to king, and since none dared to annul them they are still in force. The monasteries are supplied with beds and bedding, food, drink and clothes, so that the monks want for nothing. This is the case everywhere. The monks devote themselves to practising virtue, reciting the scriptures or sitting in meditation. When a monk from elsewhere arrives, the resident monks welcome him and carry his robes and alms-bowl for him. They also bring water to wash his feet and oil to anoint them, and offer him a collation. * After he has rested, they ask him how long he has been ordained and provide him with a room, bedding and other things according to Buddhist law.

Wherever monks live they build stupas in honour of the saints Sariputra, Maudgalaputra and Ananda,** also in honour of the Abbidharma or *Buddhist Commentaries*, the *Monastic Rules* and the Sutras. A month after the summer retirement, all devout families collect offerings for the monks and supply them with collations, while the monks hold a great assembly to expound the Law. The assembly at an end, they offer all manner of incense and flowers at the stupa of Sariputra, and keep the lamps there burning throughout the night. Actors are hired to perform a play in which Sariputra, who was originally a Brahman, goes to Bud-

---

* According to Buddhist rules, one should take no meal after noon. One could, however, partake of light refreshments such as honey or fruit juice.
** Three disciples of Buddha.

dha to ask for ordination. The lives of Maudgalaputra and Kasyapa are also performed in this way.

Most nuns present offerings at the stupa of Ananda, for it was he who entreated Buddha to allow women to take orders. The novices for the most part present offerings to Rahula, the teachers of the *Buddhist Commentaries* to the commentaries, and the teachers of the *Monastic Rules* to the rules. These offerings are made once a year, each on its appointed day. Followers of the Mahayana School make their offerings to the saints Prajnaparamita, Manjusri and Avalokitesvara.

When the monks have received their yearly offerings, the elders, laymen, Brahmans and others bring all manner of robes and necessities to offer to them. And the monks also make offerings to one another. These rituals and rules of conduct for holy monks have been handed down without interruption since Buddha's Nirvana.

After passing the Indus River, proceeding towards southern India, it is forty to fifty thousand *li* to the sea in the south. And all this land is flat, without great mountains or valleys, having only rivers and streams.

The Country of Samkasya

Eighteen *yojanas* towards the southeast there is a country called Samkasya, where Buddha descended from the Highest Heaven after ascending to preach the Law to his mother for three months. Buddha went up to heaven by the exercise of supernatural power, unknown to his disciples. Before the elapse of seven days, through his supernatural power he flew, and thus Aniruddha with his divine sight saw the Blessed One afar.

"You may go to salute the Blessed One," said Aniruddha to the Venerable Maudgalaputra.

Accordingly Maudgalaputra went to worship at Buddha's feet and exchanged greetings with him.

This done, Buddha said to him, "After seven days I shall descend to Jambudvipa." *

Then Maudgalaputra returned to earth.

At this time, the great kings, ministers and people of the eight countries round were all eager to see Buddha, having been deprived of the sight of him for so long, and they assembled like clouds to wait for the Blessed One.

Then a nun by the name of Utpala thought: "Now the kings, ministers and people have all come here to meet Buddha. I am only a woman — how can I see him first?"

Thereupon, by means of supernatural power, she transformed herself into a holy, universal monarch, ** and as such she was the very first to render homage to Buddha.

When Buddha descended from the Highest Heaven, three gem-studded ladders appeared in the air, and Buddha walked down the ladder in the centre, which was made of the seven precious substances. *** The god Brahma caused a white silver ladder to ap-

---

* The ancient Indians believed that the world consisted of four continents, the continent in the south being Jambudvipa, or India.

** The Wheel King, Chakravartti Raja or Universal Monarch, ruled over one continent or more.

*** Gold, silver, lapis-lazuli, crystal, beryl, red pearls, and agates.

pear at the right side, and on this, holding a white duster in his hand, he attended Buddha. The god Sakra caused a bright gold ladder to appear at the left side, on which, holding a parasol made of the seven precious substances, he attended Buddha. Countless devas followed Buddha to earth. When Buddha had come down, all three ladders disappeared into the ground, only seven steps remaining visible. Afterwards King Asoka, * wishing to know how deep into the ground the ladders had penetrated, sent men to dig down and find out. They went on digging till they reached the Yellow Spring at the base of the earth, yet still did not reach the bottom. This increased the king's faith and reverence, and he built a temple over the steps. On the central step he placed a full-length statue of Buddha sixteen feet high. Behind the temple he erected a stone pillar thirty cubits high, on the top of which he placed the figure of a lion. On the four sides of the pillar, which was clear and transparent as glass, images of Buddha were carved.

Once a heretical teacher came to the monks and contested their right to live here.

Defeated in argument, the monks prayed together: "If this is where we should live, let there be some miracle to prove it!"

As they uttered this prayer, the lion on top of the pillar gave a loud roar as a sign. Then the heretic was frightened and, humbled, went away.

---

* A famous Indian monarch of the third century BC.

After living on heavenly food for three months, Buddha's body emitted a heavenly fragrance, very different from that of men. So at once he took a bath, and a bathhouse was built here by men of later years, the same which is there today. A stupa was also built at the spot where the nun Utpala was the first to worship Buddha. There are also stupas at the places where Buddha cut his hair and pared his nails, as well as where the three former Buddhas and Sakyamuni Buddha* sat or walked, and wherever there were images or traces of the Buddhas. These stupas still remain. A stupa was also built where Lord Sakra and the god Brahma came down to earth with Buddha. Here are about a thousand monks and nuns, who take their meals together and study both Mahayana and Hinayana Buddhism. At their dwelling-place is a white-eared dragon that acts as their patron. It brings this region rich harvests and rain in season and preserves it from all misfortunes, so that the monks may live in security. The monks, grateful for its favours, have built a house for the dragon and provided it with a seat. Moreover, sacrificial food is prepared and offered to it, and every day three monks are selected to take their meal in the dragon's house. At the end of each summer retirement, the dragon often assumes the form of a little serpent whose ears are edged with white. The monks, recognizing it, place it in a copper vessel filled with curds, and carry it around from the highest seat to the lowest as if to pay greetings to all. After mak-

---

* Buddhists believe that a Buddha appears from time to time in the world to preach the true doctrine. After a certain lapse of time this teaching is corrupted and lost, and is not restored till a new Buddha appears. In Europe, Buddha is used to designate Sakyamuni (Gautama) Buddha. The three former Buddhas were Krakuchchanda, Kanakamuni and Kasyapa.

ing the rounds it disappears. It comes out once every year.

This country is rich and fertile, with a people prosperous and happy beyond compare. The men of other lands, coming here, are entertained and provided with all they need.

The Temple of Agnidagdha

Fifty *yojanas* north of this monastery is a temple called Agnidagdha. Agnidagdha was formerly an evil spirit, whom Buddha converted. After this conversion, people built a temple at this spot and offered it to the Arhat. Once, when the Arhat washed his hands here, some drops of water fell on the ground, the traces of which are still apparent. In spite of constant sweeping, they have never disappeared.

Here there is another stupa for Buddha, which is always swept and kept clean by good spirits without the help of men.

"Since you spirits have this ability," said a heretical king, "I shall station a large body of troops here, who will pile up dirt and filth. Will you be able to clear all that away?"

But the spirits caused a great wind to spring up, which blew the place clean.

There are a hundred small stupas here, but no one can count the actual number even if he spends a whole day trying. If he insists on knowing the number, he can place a man by the side of each stupa and then count the men. But still there will sometimes be more and sometimes less, and it will be impossible to tell the number exactly.

There is another monastery here where six to seven hundred monks live. This is where a Pratyeka Buddha once fed, and here is the place — about the size of a cart-wheel — where he entered Nirvana. Grass grows all around, but not on that spot; neither does it grow on the place where he sunned his clothes. The marks made by the stripes on his clothes can still be seen on the ground.

The City of Kanauj and the Village of Hari

Fa Xian stayed in the Dragon's House for the summer retirement, and when summer was over travelled seven *yojanas* towards the southeast, to the city of Kanauj. This city is on the Ganges and has two monasteries, both belonging to the Hinayana School. Six or seven *li* to the west of the city, on the northern bank of the Ganges, is a place where Buddha expounded the Law to his disciples. Tradition has it that here he discoursed upon impermanence and pain, the likeness of the body to a bubble or foam, and other similar matters. A stupa was built there which remains to this day.

Crossing the Ganges and continuing three *yojanas* towards the south, they reached a village called Hari, in which stupas were built at the places where Buddha preached the Law, where he walked and where he sat.

The Great Country of Vaisakha

Going southeast for ten *yojanas*, they reached the great country of Vaisakha. Outside the South Gate of the city of Vaisakha and on the east side of the road is the place where Buddha planted a willow twig which he had used to clean his teeth with. This willow grew to exactly seven feet, and thereafter never increased or diminished. Excited by envy and jealousy, heretical Brahmans would often cut it down or uproot it and throw it far away; but another willow always sprang up in the same place as before. Here too they built stupas where the four Buddhas walked and sat. The ruins are there to this day.

The City of Sravasti in the Country of Kosala and the Jetavana Retreat

Travelling northward for eight *yojanas*, they reached the city of Sravasti in the country of Kosala. This city is sparsely populated, having only about two hundred families in it. It was under the rule of King Prasenajit. Stupas were later built in this city on the sites of the ruined monastery of Mahaprajapati and the home of the elder Sudatta, and over the spots where Augulimalya attained sainthood and was cremated after he entered Nirvana. Out of jealousy, heretical Brahmans planned to destroy these stupas; but the heavens thundered and lightning flashed so that they were foiled.

About 1,200 paces out of the South Gate of this city and on the west side of the road is a temple built by the elder Sudatta. Its door faces east and it has two chambers before which stand two stone pillars. On the top of the left pillar is the image of a wheel, and on the top of the right one the image of an ox. The water in the pool is clear, the trees and plants luxuriant, and flowers of many colours make a lovely sight. This place is called the Jetavana Retreat.

When Buddha ascended the Highest Heaven to preach the Law to his mother for ninety days, King Prasenajit, eager to see his face, carved an image of him out of *gosirsha* sandalwood[*] and placed it on the seat on which Buddha usually sat. When Buddha returned to the retreat, the image left its seat and went out to meet him.

"You may keep that seat," said Buddha. "After my Nirvana you will be the model from which my followers of the four groups[**] will make images."

Upon hearing this, the image returned to its seat. This was the first image ever made of Buddha, and later generations copied it.

Then Buddha moved to a smaller dwelling on the south, about twenty paces from the one occupied by this image.

The Jetavana Retreat originally had seven storeys. And the rulers and citizens of many countries vied with one another in making offerings here, hanging silk pennants and canopies, scattering flowers and lighting lamps which burned day and night without ever being extinguished. Then a rat carried off the wick

---

[*] The finest variety of sandalwood.

[**] i.e. monks, nuns, laymen and laywomen.

from one lamp in its mouth, thereby setting fire to the flowers, pennants and canopies. The whole seven-storey building went up in flames. The rulers and citizens of all the countries round lamented bitterly, thinking that the sandalwood image must also have been burned. But four or five days later, when they opened the door of the small dwelling on the east, they were amazed and overjoyed to find the image unscathed. Together they rebuilt the retreat as a two-storey building, and moved the image back to its original place.

On arriving at the Jetavana Retreat, when Fa Xian and Dao Zheng reflected that the Blessed One had practised asceticism here for twenty-five years, they regretted having been born in a far-off country. Of the companions who had travelled with them through many lands, some had returned to their homes and some had died. As they gazed at the places where Buddha could no longer be seen, they were deeply moved and their hearts were filled with sorrow.

The monks there came forward to question them.

"Where do you come from?" they asked.

"We come from China," replied Fa Xian and Dao Zheng.

"How wonderful," exclaimed the monks, "that men from a far-off country should come all this way to seek for the Law!" And they commented to each other: "Not from the earliest times has any of our teachers ever seen a Chinese monk here!"

Four *li* to the northwest of this retreat is a wood named The Wood of Sight Restored. There had been five hundred blind men living near this retreat, but when Buddha preached to them they all recovered their sight and were so overjoyed that they drove their staffs into the ground and prostrated themselves to pay homage to Buddha. The staffs took root in the earth and grew into trees, and out of respect no one ventured to cut them down. Thus the place became a wood, and was named The Wood of Sight Restored. Here the monks of the Jetavana Retreat often go after their midday meal to sit in meditation.

Six or seven *li* northeast of the Jetavana Retreat is the site of the monastery Mother Vaisakha built for Buddha and his monks. The ruins can still be seen.

The spacious grounds of the Jetavana Retreat have two gates, one facing east and the other north. It was in this garden that the elder Sudatta covered the ground with gold coins to buy the site for Buddha. The retreat is at the centre of the garden, and Buddha spent longer here than in any other place. Stupas, each with a distinctive name, have been built where he preached for the salvation of men, and where he walked and sat. Here too is the spot where the courtesan Sundari was murdered in order to slander Buddha. *

Seventy paces north of the east gate of Jetavana Garden, on the west of the road is the place where Buddha debated with the followers of ninety-six heretical sects. The king, his ministers and the lay Buddhists all gathered to hear the disputation. An envious woman heretic named Chinchimana fastened a bundle of clothes to her belly to make it appear as if she were with child. Then before the whole assembly she accused Buddha of evil conduct. On seeing this, the king of the gods Sakra transformed himself into a white mouse and nibbled through her sash so that

---

* Some heretics sent Sundari regularly to listen to Buddha preaching. Later they murdered her and buried her corpse in Jetavana Garden, and then announced that Buddha had killed her to conceal his illicit relationship with her.

the bundle fell to the ground. The earth gaped, and she fell alive
into hell. Here too is the spot where Devadatta, who poisoned
his nails in order to murder Buddha, also fell alive into hell. All
these places were marked by later generations. At the spot where
the disputation with the heretics took place, a shrine about sixty
feet high was also built, containing an image of Buddha seated.

On the east of the road is a temple named "Overshadowed".
This is also about sixty feet in height and was built by Brahman
heretics just opposite the shrine erected over the debating place.
This temple is so named because, when the sun is in the west, the
shadow of the Buddhist shrine covers the heretics' temple; but
when the sun is in the east, the shadow of the heretics' temple
falls towards the north and can never overshadow the Buddhist
shrine.

The heretics sent men regularly to look after their temple,
sweep it, water it, burn incense, light the lamps and present offerings. But by the morning their lamps always disappeared, and
they would discover them in the Buddhist shrine. The Brahmans
grew angry, and said, "The monks are taking our lamps to offer
to Buddha. We must stop them." So they kept a watch by night.
Then they saw the gods they worshipped take the lamps, circle
the Buddhist shrine three times, offer the lamps before the image
of Buddha, then suddenly disappear. At that the Brahmans realized that Buddha was greater than their gods, and they forsook
their homes to become his followers. It was said that this had occurred only recently.

Around the Jetavana Retreat are ninety-eight monasteries, of
which all but one are occupied by monks.

In the Middle Kingdom there are ninety-six heretical sects,

who claim to know not only the present but the future. Each sect has its disciples, who also ask for alms but do not use alms-bowls. They also do good deeds, building hospices by the side of solitary roads to provide shelter, bedding, food and drink for wayfarers, monks and passers-by. But their aim in doing this is not like that of the Buddhists.

Here are also Devadatta's disciples, who make offerings to the three former Buddhas but not to Sakyamuni Buddha.

Four *li* southeast of the city of Sravasti is the place where Buddha stood by the roadside when King Virudhaka set out to attack the Sakya clan. A stupa has been built to mark the spot.

Fifty *li* to the west of this city, they reached a town called Tadwa, where Kasyapa Buddha was born, where he met his father and where he entered Nirvana. Stupas have been built at all these places. A large stupa has also been built over the remains of Kasyapa Buddha.

The Town of Napika, the City of Kapilavastu and the Garden of Lumbini

Travelling twelve *yojanas* southeast from the city of Sravasti, they arrived at a town called Napika, where Krakuchchanda Buddha was born, met his father and entered Nirvana. Monasteries and stupas have been built at these places.

Less than one *yojana* to the north they reached the town where Kanakamuni Buddha was born, met his father and entered

Nirvana. Stupas have been built at all these places.

Less than one *yojana* to the east they reached the city of Kapilavastu. This city has neither king nor citizens, and looks completely deserted; for here live only some monks and a few dozen families of the laity. Among the ruins of the palace of King Suddhodana is an image of the prince's mother, showing the prince, * riding on a white elephant, coming to enter his mother's womb. A stupa has been built over the spot where the prince, having left the city by the East Gate, saw a sick man and ordered his charioteer to drive back to the palace. Here too are the places where Asita observed the marks on the prince, and where the prince with Nanda and others brought down an elephant. An arrow shot from here entered the earth thirty *li* to the southeast, causing a fountain to spring up; and the people made a well from which wayfarers might drink. Stupas have also been built at the following places: where Buddha returned to see his father after attaining Buddha-hood; where the earth quaked six times when five hundred men of the Sakya clan saluted Upali after renouncing their homes; where Buddha expounded the Law to devas while the four celestial kings guarded the four gates of the hall so that his father, the king, could not enter; and where Buddha sat facing east under a *nyagrodha* tree — which is growing to this day — while Mahaprajapati offered him a robe. Here also can be found the stupa built at the place where King Virudhaka slaughtered the descendants of the Sakya clan, who had all attained to the first stage of sainthood. A few *li* to the northeast of the city is the royal field where the prince sat under a tree to

_____

* i.e. Buddha.

watch men ploughing. Fifty *li* to the east of the city is the royal garden called Lumbini. It was in this garden that the queen entered the pond to bathe. After bathing she came out from the northern side of the pond, walked for about twenty paces and, holding the branch of a tree and facing east, gave birth to a princely son. As soon as the prince was born he took seven steps, and was bathed by two dragon-kings. A well has been made at that bathing place, and monks often drink the water from it as well as from the pond.

Four places are always determined in advance: where Buddhas shall attain Buddha-hood; where they shall begin to preach; where they shall expound the Law and refute heretics; and where they shall descend from the Highest Heaven after having preached to their mothers. Other places are chosen according to circumstances.

The country of Kapilavastu is deserted and few people travel its roads for fear of the white elephants and lions there. One cannot journey without taking great precautions.

The Country of Ramagrama

Five *yojanas* east of Buddha's birthplace lies the country of Ramagrama. The king of this country obtained a share of the relics of Buddha, and upon his return home built a stupa named Ramagrama. Beside this stupa is a pond in which lives a dragon that keeps constant guard over the stupa and worships there day and night. When King Asoka was living, he determined to demolish eight stupas and built 84,000 new ones; and having pulled down seven, he came to raze this of Ramagrama. But then the dragon appeared and took him to its palace, where it showed him all the vessels it used in worship.

"If your vessels are better than mine," it said to the king, "then destroy this stupa and take it away, and I will not quarrel with you."

Knowing that the dragon's vessels were not of this world, King Asoka had to go home.

Since this place was completely deserted, there was no one to sweep and water it. But a herd of elephants would often come with water in their trunks to water the ground, and they offered fragrant blossoms of many kinds here. A monk who came from another country to worship at this stupa was terrified at the sight of the elephants, and hid behind a tree. But when he saw these beasts presenting offerings in the approved manner, he was deeply moved to think that there were no monks here to look after this stupa and that it was left to the elephants to keep it clean. He hereupon gave up his status as a fully ordained monk to take up the duties of a novice, cutting the weeds and brambles himself and levelling the ground, till all was in good order. This done, he urged the king to build a monastery there, and volunteered to be the abbot of it. There are monks now living there. This occurred recently, and the abbot of this monastery has always been a novice since that time.

Three *yojanas* east of this is the place where the prince dismissed Chandaka and his white horse. A stupa has also been built here.

Travelling east again for four *yojanas*, they arrived at the Ashes Stupa, where there is also a monastery.

The City of Kusinagara

Twelve *yojanas* further east, they reached the city of Kusinagara. It was north of this city, between two trees beside the Hiranyavati River, that Buddha entered Nirvana with his head towards the north. Here are stupas and monasteries which were built at the following places: where Subhadra, Buddha's last disciple, entered the Order; where the Blessed One, lying in a golden coffin, received homage for seven days; where Vajrapani laid down his golden mace; and where the eight kings shared the relics of Buddha. This city is almost deserted, with only a handful of monks and a few laymen as its inhabitants.

The Last Farewell of the Lichchhavis to Buddha

Travelling twelve *yojanas* to the southeast, they reached the spot where the Lichchhavis wished to follow Buddha to the place of his Nirvana, but could not gain his consent. Out of affection for him they would not go away; so Buddha made a deep ditch appear which they were unable to cross. He then gave them his alms-bowl as a relic, and sent them home. A stone pillar with inscriptions was erected at this place.

The Country of Vaisali, the Stupa of Bows and Lances Laid Down, and the Council for Collating the Monastic Rules

Continuing five *yojanas* to the east, they arrived at the country of Vaisali. North of the city of Vaisali is the storeyed Monastery of the Great Forest in which Buddha lived and the stupa built for half the relics of Ananda. In this city also dwelt the Lady Amrapali, who built a stupa for Buddha, the ruins of which may still be seen today.

West of the road three *li* to the south of the city is the garden which the Lady Amrapali offered to Buddha as a dwelling-place.

When Buddha was approaching the time of his Nirvana, he left Vaisali with his disciples by the West Gate and, turning to his right, looked back at the city and said: "This is the last place I shall have visited." Later a stupa was built on that spot.

Three *li* northwest of the city is the Stupa of Bows and Lances Laid Down, which received this name because of the following happenings:

In the upper reaches of the Ganges lived a king, one of whose inferior wives gave birth to an unformed foetus. The queen, who was jealous, said: "You have given birth to an omen of misfortune."

Then they put the foetus in a chest, and threw it into the Ganges.

Another king, who was then on a pleasure trip in the lower reaches of the Ganges, saw the chest floating in the river. Having brought it ashore and opened it, he found it contained a thousand handsome, royal-looking infants. The king brought them up and they grew into brave, strong warriors, who conquered every country they attacked. And at last they came to attack their father's kingdom. The king was so greatly dismayed that his inferior wife asked what had caused him such alarm.

"The king of a neighbouring state has a thousand sons," he told her. "They are all brave and strong beyond compare, and now they are coming to attack us. That is why I am alarmed."

"Do not let that alarm you, O King," she said. "If you build a high pavilion on the east of the city and place me on it when the invaders come, I shall be able to quell them."

The king did as she proposed. And when the invaders came the inferior wife called to them from the top of the pavilion.

"You are all my sons," she cried. "What makes you so rebellious?"

"Who are you that claim to be our mother?" they asked.

"If you do not believe me," she said, "look up, and open your mouths."

Then she pressed her breasts with both hands, and from each breast gushed five hundred jets of milk, which spurted into the mouths of her thousand sons. Thereupon the invaders realized that she was indeed their mother, and laid down their bows and lances.

Meditating on this event, both the kings became Pratyeka Buddhas. The two stupas built in their honour are standing today.

After his accession to Buddha-hood, Buddha informed his disciples: "This is where I laid down my bow and lance."

When the people knew this, they built a stupa there, and gave it this name.

The thousand sons were in fact the thousand Buddhas of this *Bhadra-kalpa*.*

By the side of the Stupa of Bows and Lances Laid Down, Buddha said to Ananda: "After another three months I shall enter Nirvana."

But Ananda was so bewitched by the king of demons at the time that he did not request Buddha to remain longer in the world.

Three or four *li* to the east of this there stands another stupa. One hundred years after Buddha's Nirvana, some monks in Vaisali began to commit the ten acts forbidden by the Law, and defended themselves by maintaining that Buddha had decreed these practices. Then the Arhats, monks, and laymen — seven hundred in all — who strictly observed the rules, edited and collated the *Monastic Rules* afresh. And a stupa was later built here, which remains to this day.

The Confluence of the Five Rivers
and the Death of Ananda

From here they journeyed eastward for four *yojanas* till they came to the confluence of the five rivers. When Ananda was

---

* A *kalpa* is a period of time. *Bhadra-kalpa* is the present cosmic age.

travelling from Magadha to Vaisali, intending to enter Nirvana there, the devas informed King Ajatasatru of it. Then the king, at the head of his troops, hastened to the bank of the river. And the Lichchhavis of Vaisali also, hearing that Ananda was coming, came to meet him on the opposite bank. Ananda reflected that if he proceeded King Ajatasatru would be grieved, while if he turned back the Lichchhavis would complain. Accordingly he went to the middle of the river where he engaged in the Fire Meditation and by this means burned himself to death. His remains were divided into two portions, one for each side of the river. Thus each of the kings had half of Ananda's relics, and they built stupas for them after returning home.

The City of Pataliputra in the Country of Magadha

After crossing the river and travelling one *yojana* south, they reached the city of Pataliputra in the country of Magadha. Pataliputra was King Asoka's capital. The royal palaces in the city were all constructed by genii and spirits. The walls and arches are of stone, with carvings and sculptures cut by no human hand. The ruins can still be seen.

The younger brother of King Asoka, having attained Arhatship, spent all his time on Gridhrakuta Mountain, where he found pleasure in quietness and repose. To show his respect, the king invited him to his palace. But since the recluse enjoyed living in the quiet hills, he declined the invitation.

"If you will consent to come," said the king, "I shall make a hill inside the city for you."

Then the king prepared food and drink and summoned genii and spirits.

"I hope you will all accept my invitation for tomorrow," he said. "But as there are no seats, I must request each of you to bring your own."

On the following day each of the great genii and spirits came with a huge boulder four or five paces square. After the feast was over, the king asked the genii and spirits to pile up these rocks to make a hill, using five boulders to form a cave underneath, about thirty feet in length, twenty in breadth and more than ten feet in height.

There was a Brahman of the Mahayana School named Radhas-vami living in this city. Intelligent and wise, he had mastered all the knowledge of his time, and he lived in a state of tranquillity. The king respected him as his religious teacher, and dared not sit in his presence whenever he paid him a call. If the king took his hand out of affection or respect, the Brahman would wash himself afterwards. Almost fifty years old, he was honoured by the whole country. It was due to this one man that Buddhism was propagated and the heretics could gain no advantages over the Buddhists.

By the side of King Asoka's stupa is a magnificent Mahayana monastery. There is also a Hinayana monastery, and in these two monasteries live six or seven hundred monks whose behaviour is most decorous and orderly. Monks of high virtue and scholars from every quarter flock here to seek for knowledge and truth. The Brahman teacher Manjusri, who is honoured by all the holy monks and devout Mahayana priests of the country, also resides in this monastery.

The Image Procession and the Charitable Hospitals

Pataliputra is the largest city in the whole Middle Kingdom. The people are rich and prosperous, and vie with each other in performing good deeds. Every year in celebration of the eighth day of the second month they hold an image procession. They use a four-wheeled cart on which five tiers are constructed in bamboo, with a halberd-shaped central post about twenty feet high, the whole structure resembling a pagoda. This is covered with white woollen cloth, painted with various devas in colour, adorned with gold, silver and glass, and hung with silk pennants and canopies. There are four shrines on the four sides, each containing a seated Buddha, attended by standing Bodhisattvas. About twenty such cars are prepared, each decked out in a different way. On the day of the procession the monks and laymen of the country assemble together to dance, play music and offer flowers and incense. The Brahmans come out to receive the images of Buddha, which are brought into the city one after the other, and remain there till the next day. Lamps burn throughout the night, and there is dancing and music to honour the gods. This ceremony is the same in all the Buddhist countries.

The elders and laymen of this country have established charitable hospitals in the city, to which all the poor, homeless, deformed and ill can go. Here all their wants are supplied, and the physicians who attend them prescribe the food and medicine they require. When cured, they are free to leave.

King Asoka, after he had destroyed seven stupas, built 84,000 new ones, the first being the great stupa three *li* or more to the south of this city. In front of this is one of Buddha's footprints, over which a temple has been erected, its door opening north towards the stupa. South of the stupa there is a stone pillar fourteen or fifteen feet around and more than thirty feet high. The inscription upon this reads:

"King Asoka offered Jambudvipa to monks from all parts of the world, then redeemed it again with silver. And this he did three times."

Three or four hundred paces north of the stupa is the site of the city of Niraya which King Asoka built, and here stands a stone pillar more than thirty feet high, with the figure of a lion above it. An inscription on the pillar relates the reason for building it and the year, the month and the day.

The Solitary Crag and the Village of Kalapinaka

Travelling southeast from here for nine *yojanas*, they arrived at a solitary crag. On the summit of the crag is a stone cell, facing south, with a seated image of Buddha in it. This is where Sakra sent the heavenly musician Panchasikha to play the harp for Buddha's pleasure, and it was here also that Sakra questioned

Buddha on forty-two points. Buddha traced a line on the rock with his finger at each question, and the marks of his finger are there to this day. There is also a monastery here.

One *yojana* to the southwest, they reached the village of Kalapinaka. This is where Sariputra was born, and here he returned to enter Nirvana. A stupa built here is standing to this day.

The New City of Rajagriha and the
  Old City of King Bimbisara

One *yojana* to the west they arrived at the new city of Rajagriha, built by King Ajatasatru. There are two monasteries here. Three hundred paces out of the West Gate of the city towers the magnificent stupa built by King Ajatasatru over the share of Buddha's relics which he obtained.

Leaving the city by the southern side and proceeding for four *li*, they entered a valley surrounded by five hills as if by a city wall. This is the site of the old city of King Bimbisara, which is five or six *li* from east to west, and seven or eight *li* from north to south. This is where Sariputra and Maudgalaputra first met Asvajit, where Nirgrantha made a fiery pit and prepared poisoned rice for Buddha, and where King Ajatasatru gave wine to a black elephant in order to injure Buddha. In the garden of Amrapali in the northeast corner of this city Jivaka built a monastery to invite Buddha and his 1,250 disciples to receive his offerings.

The ruins still remain. But the city is desolate without inhabitants.

Gridhrakuta Mountain

After entering the valley and travelling fifteen *li* to the mountains in the southeast, they reached Gridhrakuta Mountain. Three *li* from the summit of the mountain is a cave facing south, in which Buddha used to sit in meditation. About thirty paces to the north west is another cave where Ananda was once sitting in meditation when Mara Pisuna took the form of a vulture and hovered in front of the cave to terrify him. But Buddha with his supernatural power stretched his hand through the rock and patted Ananda's shoulder, so that his fears were allayed. The traces of the vulture and the hole made by Buddha's hand can still be seen today. Thus the name of this mountain is the Mountain of the Vulture Cave. In front of the cave is the place where the four Buddhas sat. The Arhats each have a cave in which to meditate — several hundred in all. Once Buddha was pacing to and fro in front of his cave when Devadatta rolled down a stone from the precipice in the north, injuring Buddha's toe. The stone is there to this day. The hall in which Buddha preached the Law has been destroyed, and only the foundations of the brick walls remain. The peaks of this mountain are beautiful and imposing, and it is the highest of all the five hills.

Fa Xian bought incense, flowers and oil for lamps in the new city, and requested two resident monks to guide him to

Gridhrakuta Mountain. There he offered the incense and flowers and lit the lamps.

"This is where Buddha used to live," he said, shedding tears of emotion. "And here he expounded the *Surangama Sutra*. Fa Xian, who was born too late to see Buddha himself, can only gaze at the traces left by him and the places where he lived."

He recited the *Surangama Sutra* in front of the cave and, after spending the night there, returned to the new city.

The Ruins in the Old Town of King Bimbisara

On the west side of the road about three hundred paces out of the North Gate of the old city stands the Retreat of the Karanda Bamboo Grove, which is kept clean by the monks there. Two or three *li* north of the retreat is a *samasana*, or burial ground.

Three hundred paces west along the southern hill is the Cave of Pippala, where Buddha used to sit in meditation after his meals. Five or six *li* further west is the Cave of Saptaparna, on the shady side of the hill. It was here that the five hundred Arhats made a compilation of the scriptures after Buddha's Nirvana. During this work, three high seats were prepared and adorned in a stately manner. Sariputra took the left seat and Maudgalaputra the right. Of the five hundred Arhats one was absent, and great Kasyapa presided over the assembly while Ananda, who was unable to enter, stood outside the gate. A stupa built at this spot remains to this day. Along the hillside are many caves used by the Arhats for meditation.

Three *li* to the east from the North Gate of the old city is the Cave of Devadatta. Fifty paces from this there is a great, square, black rock. Once a monk paced this rock, meditating on the impermanence, sorrow and vanity of life. Conscious of human impurity, he loathed his body and drawing his knife longed to kill himself, but then remembered that the Blessed One had made a rule forbidding suicide. He reflected, however, that though this was so, he would only be killing the Three Mortal Foes, * and so he cut his throat. When his knife gashed the flesh, he attained to the stage of Srotapanna; when his throat was half severed, he realized the sainthood of Anagamin; and when he had made an end of himself, he achieved Arhatship and entered Nirvana.

The City of Gaya

Travelling west from here for four *yojanas*, they reached the city of Gaya. This city is desolate and completely deserted.

Going another twenty *li* south, they arrived at the place where Buddha lived as an ascetic for six years. This district is richly wooded.

Three *li* to the west, they visited the spot where Buddha bathed once and a deva lowered the branch of a tree so as to help him out of the water.

Two *li* to the north, they reached the place where the maidens

---

* Lust, hatred and ignorance.

of Gramika offered milk and rice to Buddha.

Two *li* further north is the spot where Buddha sat facing east on a rock under a great tree to eat the rice. Both the tree and the rock are still there. The rock is about six feet square and two feet high. As the climate in the Middle Kingdom is temperate, a tree may grow for several thousand or even ten thousand years.

From here they proceeded northeast for half a *yojana*, till they came to the cave which Buddha entered and in which he sat cross-legged facing the west. He reflected that if he were going to attain to Buddha-hood, there should be some divine manifestation. Then the shadow of a Buddha about three feet high — which is still distinctly visible — appeared on the rock wall. At the same time heaven and earth quaked, and devas in the air proclaimed:

"This is not the place for Buddhas of the past or the future to attain to Buddha-hood. In the southwest, under a *pattra* tree less than half a *yojana* from here, is the place for Buddhas of the past and the future to attain to Buddha-hood!"

This said, the devas led the way forward, singing, and Buddha rose and followed them. Thirty paces from the tree, the devas presented him with *kusa* grass, which he accepted. When he had advanced another fifteen paces, five hundred blue birds came flying towards him, encircled him three times and flew away. Having reached the *pattra* tree, he spread the *kusa* grass on the ground and sat down facing the east. Then Mara the demon king sent three beautiful girls from the north to tempt him, and led troops from the south to try him. But Buddha pressed his toe on the ground, and Mara's soldiers retreated in confusion while the three girls turned into old women.

At all these places visited by Buddha while he lived as an ascetic for six years, and at each spot subsequently mentioned, men of later times have built stupas and set up images of Buddha, which exist to this very day. Stupas have also been built at the following places: where Buddha, seven days after his accession to Buddha-hood, looked at the tree and enjoyed the bliss of emancipation; where he walked from east to west for seven days under the *pattra* tree; where the devas raised a terrace of the seven precious substances to make offerings to Buddha for seven days; where the blind dragon Muchilinda revolved around Buddha for seven days; where Buddha sat on a square rock facing east under a *nyagrodha* tree when Brahma came to invite him; where the four celestial kings presented him with his alms-bowl; where the five hundred merchants offered him flour and honey; and where he converted the Kasyapa brothers and their thousand disciples.

There are three monasteries at the place where Buddha attained to Buddha-hood, all of which are occupied by monks. These monks are supported by the local people who supply them liberally with all they need, so that they lack for nothing. The *Monastic Rules* are strictly kept, and they also observe with decorum the ritual of sitting, rising and taking part in assemblies practised by the holy monks during Buddha's lifetime.

Good care has been taken of the four great stupas ever since Buddha's Nirvana. The four great stupas stand at the place where Buddha was born, where he attained Buddha-hood, where he began to preach, and where he entered Nirvana.

The Hell of King Asoka

When King Asoka was a child in a former life, while playing on the road he met Sakyamuni Buddha begging for alms. Delighted, he offered Buddha a handful of earth, which Buddha took to spread on the ground where he used to walk. As a result of this good deed, the child became King of the Iron Wheel and ruled over Jambudvipa. Once, while making a tour of inspection in Jambudvipa, he saw the hell between two iron-encircled hills where the wicked are punished.

"What place is that?" he asked his ministers.

"That is where Yama, the king of spirits, punishes the wicked," they told him.

On hearing this, Asoka reflected that if the king of spirits could make a hell to punish the wicked, why should not he, a ruler of men, make a place of punishment for criminals?

So he asked his ministers: "Who can make a hell for me and take charge of punishing evil-doers there?"

"Only the most wicked man can do that," they replied.

Thereupon the king sent his ministers out in all directions to look for wicked men. Eventually they found a man by the side of a pond who was tall, strong and swarthy, with yellow hair and blue eyes. He could catch fish with his feet, and make birds and beasts come when he called; but then he shot them, not sparing a single one. Having found this man, they sent him to the king.

"Make a square enclosure with high walls," the king charged him secretly. "Plant it with a profusion of flowers and fruit trees and build a handsomely ornamented bathing pool, so that passers-by will be eager to look inside. Make the doors and windows strong. Whenever anyone enters, put him to every torture you can devise and do not let him out again. Even if I should enter the place myself, you must torture me as well, and never let me go. Now I appoint you the keeper of this hell."

Once a monk who was begging from door to door entered the gate of this hell, and the keeper promptly seized him and prepared to torture him. But the terrified monk pleaded with him and was granted a brief respite to have his mid-day meal. At that moment another man came in, and the keeper immediately put him into a mortar and pounded him till a red froth appeared. Having witnessed this, the monk reflected on the impermanence, sorrow and vanity of bodily existence, which is like a bubble or foam upon the water. And so he achieved Arhatship. Thus when the keeper seized and thrust him into a cauldron of boiling water, the monk was glad at heart and his face was serene. The fire went out, the water cooled, and up sprang a lotus flower with the monk sitting upon it.

The keeper went to inform the king of this.

"Something amazing has happened in hell," he said. "Will Your Majesty please go and have a look?"

"I dare not," replied Asoka. "Remember our former agreement."

"This is no small matter, sire," protested the keeper. "Never mind that agreement, but come with me at once."

So the king followed him to the hell. Then the monk expounded the Law to King Asoka, who accepted the faith, destroyed this hell and repented of all the crimes he had committed. From that time on the believed in and respected the Three Precious

Gems,* and often repaired to a *pattra* tree under which he repented his sins and observed the Eight Precepts.**

"Where is it the king always goes?" inquired the queen.

"His Majesty often goes to the *pattra* tree," replied the ministers.

Then the queen sent someone to fell the tree when Asoka was not there. When he came and saw what had happened, he fell senseless to the ground. His ministers dashed water in his face and eventually he recovered consciousness. He piled up bricks round the stump of the tree and watered its root with a hundred pitchers of milk, then prostrated himself on the ground and vowed:

"If the tree does not grow, I shall never rise again!"

As he uttered this vow the tree began to grow till it reached its present height, which is nearly a hundred feet.

The Kukkutapada Mountain

Continuing three *li* to the south, they reached the mountain called Kukkutapada. Kasyapa is at present in this mountain. He split the mountain to enter it, but that opening is now closed. And his body is preserved entire in a chasm at a great distance from this in one side of the mountain. Outside the chasm is the

---

* Buddha, Dharma and Sangha.
** Not to kill, not to steal, not to have sexual intercourse, not to tell lies, not to drink wine, not to use cosmetics and personal adornments or to dance and play music, not to sleep on fine beds, and not to take food in the afternoon.

place where he washed his hands. If the people of this country suffer from headaches, they rub the earth from this spot on their heads and the pain is cured. Since Kasyapa's Nirvana Arhats have lived in this mountain, and each year the monks of neighbouring states go there to worship Kasyapa. If anyone comes with doubts in his mind, some Arhat will appear to reason with him by night, disappearing as soon as his doubts have been resolved. This mountain is thickly overgrown with brambles, and is so infested with lions, tigers and wolves that one cannot wander there freely.

The City of Benares and the Deer Park

Fa Xian returned to Pataliputra and, travelling west along the Ganges for ten *yojanas*, arrived at a monastery called Atavi in which Buddha once lived. There are monks in residence now.

Again proceeding west along the Ganges for twelve *yojanas*, he reached the city of Benares in the country of Kasi. About ten *li* northeast of the city is the Deer Park Retreat of the Rishis. Originally a Pratyeka Buddha lived in this park, and wild deer often came here for shelter. When the Blessed One was about to become a Buddha, devas announced from the sky:

"The son of King Suddhodana, who renounced his home to acquire supreme truth, will attain to Buddha-hood after seven days."

On hearing this, the Pratyeka Buddha entered Nirvana. Therefore his place is called the Deer Park of the Rishis. After the Blessed One's accession to Buddha-hood, men of later ages built a retreat here. Buddha wished to convert Kaundinya and his four companions, but these five men said to each other:

"For six years this monk Gautama lived as an ascetic on one grain of sesame and one of rice a day, yet he did not obtain the truth. Now that he is living among men, having thrown off all mental and physical restraints, what truth can he have obtained? If he comes today, let us be sure not to speak to him."

When Buddha arrived, however, the five men felt impelled to rise and salute him.

Sixty paces further north is the place where Buddha sat facing east when he preached his first sermon and converted Kaundinya and his companions. Twenty paces north of this is the place where Buddha predicted the future of Maitreya. Fifty paces to the south is the spot where the dragon Elapatra asked Buddha when he could be freed from his dragon form. Stupas built at all these spots are standing to this day. There are also two monasteries, both of which are occupied by monks. Thirteen *yojanas* northwest of the Deer Park Retreat is the country of Kausambi. The monastery there is called the Garden of Ghoshira, and here Buddha once lived. Most of the monks in residence at present study Hinayana Buddhism.

Eight *yojanas* to the east is the spot where Buddha converted an evil demon. Stupas also mark where he lived, walked and sat. A hundred monks or more live in the monastery here.

The Country of Dakshina and the
Paravati Monastery

Proceeding south for two hundred *yojanas*, they came to the country called Dakshina. Here is a monastery of the former Kasyapa Buddha, hewn out of a great mountain of rock. It has five tiers: the first in the shape of an elephant, with five hundred chambers; the second in the shape of a lion, with four hundred chambers; the third in the shape of a horse, with three hundred chambers; the fourth in the shape of an ox, with two hundred chambers; and the fifth in the shape of a dove, with one hundred chambers. At the very top there is a spring of water which flows down in front of the chambers through a circuitous channel till it reaches the lowest tier, then, passing the chambers, issues at last through the door. A window has been hewn in the rock of every chamber in each tier; thus they receive ample light and no corner is dark. At the four corners of this edifice steps have been hewn in the rock. Since men of the present time are short, they have to climb the stairway, while the men of old could reach the top in one step. This monastery's name is Paravati, which means "dove". There have always been Arhats here. The land is barren and void of inhabitants.

At a great distance from the hill is a village in which all the inhabitants are monks or Brahmans who hold heretical views and do not believe in Buddhism, or are followers of other heretical schools.

The people of this country often see men flying to the monastery here. Thus they ask those monks who come from abroad to worship here:

"Why don't you fly? All the monks we see here can fly."

The monks then answer evasively: "Our wings have not yet grown!"

The roads in Dakshina are dangerous and hard to travel. Even those who hear of the place and wish to go there have to present money or goods to the king of the country, who then appoints men as their guides who will pass them on from one post to another in order to show them the way. Fa Xian was unable to go there. He has related simply what men of that country told him.

The Sanskrit Scriptures and the Sanskrit Language

Travelling east from Benares they returned to Pataliputra. Fa Xian had come to seek the books of monastic discipline, but in the countries of North India these rules are handed down by word of mouth, hence there were no written records for him to copy. He had therefore to travel as far as Central India, where in a Mahayana monastery he obtained a collection of the precepts of monastic discipline. It was the *Rules of the Mahasanghika*, which were first observed by the great assembly of monks while Buddha was yet alive. This copy has been handed down in the Jetavana Retreat. Though each of the eighteen sects has its own rules of conduct, they agree in all essentials, simply paying more or less attention to certain minor matters. But this book is the most comprehensive. He also obtained a copy of the rules in about 7,000 verses. This was the *Rules of the Sarvastivadah* —

the same rules as those observed by monks in China — which was also handed down orally from teacher to pupil without being committed to writing. In this monastery he also obtained a copy of the *Samyuktabhidharma-hridaya Sastra* in about 6,000 verses, a copy of the *Nirvana Sutra* in 2,500 verses, a copy of the *Vaipulya-parinirvana Sutra* in about 5,000 verses, and a copy of the *Commentaries of the Mahasanghika*.

Fa Xian spent three years in studying written and spoken Sanskrit and in copying these books.

Upon arriving at the Middle Kingdom and seeing the excellent rules and decorous conduct of the monks here in their daily life, Dao Zheng sighed over the imperfect rules of the monks in faraway China and prayed that never again might he be reborn in a far-off country till he should attain to Buddha-hood. So he settled down in India and never returned to China. But Fa Xian had gone there in order to bring back the *Monastic Rules* to China, so he returned, alone.

The Great Country of Champa
and the Kingdom of Tamralipti

Eighteen *yojanas* to the east along the Ganges, on the south bank of the river, is the great country of Champa. Stupas have been built at Buddha's dwelling-place, where he walked and where the four Buddhas sat. There are monks living there.

Nearly fifty *yojanas* to the east, Fa Xian reached Tamralipti which borders on the sea. Here there are twenty-four monasteries, all with monks living in them, and Buddhism flourishes. After staying here for two years to copy sutras and make drawings of Buddha's images, he set sail in a large merchant ship across the ocean towards the southwest. Taking advantage of the fair wind of early winter, the vessel sailed for fourteen days and nights till it reached Simhala, the Country of the Lion.

Simhala, the Country of the Lion

The people of Simhala informed Fa Xian that the distance of the voyage was about seven hundred *yojanas*. The Country of the Lion is an island some fifty *yojanas* from east to west and thirty from north to south. To its left and right are about a hundred small islands, ten, twenty or two hundred *li* from each other, all of which are under the rule of this large island. Most of these islands produce precious stones and pearls, and there is a district of about ten square *li* which produces the *mani* jewel. The king has posted guards here, and takes a levy of three-tenths of the jewels that are found.

There were originally no inhabitants here, only spirits and dragons. When merchants from other countries came to trade, the spirits did not appear, but simply set out their rare merchandise with the prices marked. The merchants paid accordingly, and took away the goods directly. Owing to this traffic of merchants, the people of all the countries round heard how pleasant a land this was, and came here too. In this way a large kingdom was formed. The climate is temperate winter and summer alike. Plants and trees bloom the whole year round, and the fields may be sown whenever the people please — there are no fixed seasons.

Buddha's Footprints and the Monastery Called Abhayagiri

Buddha once came to this country to convert a wicked dragon. With his supernatural power, he planted one foot at the north of the royal city and one on a mountain top fifteen *yojanas* away. Over the footprint north of the royal city, a great stupa four hundred feet high was built, adorned with gold and silver and studded with all kinds of jewels. By the side of this stupa a monastery was erected which is called Abhayagiri (The Hill of Fearlessness), and here are five thousand monks. It contains a hall for the worship of Buddha, engraved with gold and silver and adorned with precious stones. In it stands an image of Buddha made of green jade, some twenty feet high. The entire image sparkles with the seven precious substances, and its splendour and magnificence defy description. In its right hand the image holds a priceless pearl.

Fa Xian had left China for many years and associated with none but men of foreign lands. All the mountains, rivers, plants and trees that he saw were strange to him. Moreover, his companions had left him — some had remained behind, while some had died. Looking at his lonely shadow, he was often filled with sadness. So when he stood by the side of this jade image and happened to see a white silk fan from China — the offering of some merchant — tears filled his eyes and he gave way to his grief.

A former king of this country had sent a messenger to the Middle Kingdom to fetch a seed of the *pattra* tree to plant beside the hall, and this grew some two hundred feet high. This tree inclined towards the southeast and, fearing that it might fall, the king set up a huge pillar that required eight or nine men to encircle it, to support the tree. At the place where the tree was propped, a branch grew out from the trunk and pierced the pillar, then sent down roots to the ground. This branch was so thick it took four men to encircle it. Though the pillar is cleft in two, since it still supports the tree it has not been removed.

Under this tree is a rest house containing a seated image of Buddha, to which both monks and laymen pay homage continuously. In this city there is also the Temple of Buddha's Tooth, constructed entirely of the seven precious substances. The king leads a pure life and observes the Buddhist precepts, while the citizens of the capital also have the greatest reverence for Buddhism. Since the establishment of this kingdom, there has been no famine or trouble here. The monks' storehouses are filled with precious stones and *mani* jewels. When the king once went to inspect these storehouses and saw the *mani* jewels, he coveted them and longed to seize them. After three days, however, he repented, and going to the monks and saluting them he confessed the evil desire he had felt.

"I hope you will make it a rule," he told the monks, "never to let the king inspect your storehouses, and admit no monk who has not been in the Order for forty years."

Buddha's Tooth and the Monastery of Bodhi

In this city are many Buddhist laymen, elders and merchants of all trades. The houses are beautiful, the roads level and trim. Preaching-halls have been built at the crossroads, where, on the eighth, fourteenth and fifteenth of each month, high seats are set, and monks, laymen and believers of the four groups gather to listen to the preaching of the Law. The people of this country say there are about 60,000 monks fed at the public expense, while the king supports five or six thousand more in the royal city. Those who need food may bring their own alms-bowls to fetch it, and carry away as much as the vessel contains.

Buddha's Tooth is usually displayed in the middle of the third month. Ten days before this event, the king adorns and caparisons a great elephant, and bids an orator in royal robes ride on this elephant and sound a drum, then make this proclamation:

"For three *Asankhyeya-kalpas*,* Buddha practised asceticism. Never sparing himself, he gave up his kingdom, his wife and son, and even tore out his eye to give to another. He cut his own flesh to deliver a dove, gave away his head as alms, offered his body to a ravenous tiger, and did not grudge his marrow and brain. Having suffered these pains for the sake of all living creatures, at last he became a Buddha. While in this world he spent forty-nine years expounding the Law and edifying the people. He gave rest to the weary, and saved those who were lost. And when he had fulfilled his mission among men, he entered Nir-

---

* Previous cosmic ages.

vana. Since his Nirvana, 1,497 years have passed, during which the Eye of the World has been closed and all living creatures have never ceased to grieve. Ten days from now, Buddha's Tooth will be brought out and carried to Abhayagiri Monastery. All monks and laymen who wish to do good deeds may level the road, adorn the lanes and streets, and prepare all kinds of flowers and incense as offerings."

After this proclamation, on both sides of the road the king sets images of the five hundred forms which Buddha assumed in his earlier existences, when, for example, he was born as Sydana, Sama, the king of the elephants, a deer and a horse. Painted and richly adorned, these images appear extremely lifelike. Then Buddha's Tooth is brought out and carried along the main road, and offerings are made to it all along the way till it reaches the hall in Abhayagiri Monastery. There monks and laymen gather to burn incense, light lamps and perform all manner of religious ceremonies day and night without rest. After ninety days, the Tooth is carried back to the temple in the city. And this temple is open on fast days so that believers may worship the Tooth according to the Buddhist custom.

Forty *li* to the east of Abhayagiri Monastery there is another hill, and on it stands a monastery called Bodhi, in which live some 2,000 monks. Among them is a monk of great virtue, by the name of Dharmakoti, whom the people of this country revere. He has lived in a stone cell for some forty years. And, such is his compassion, he can make serpents and mice live together without injuring each other.

Mahavihara Monastery

Seven *li* to the south of this city is Mahavihara Monastery, where live 3,000 monks. There was once a monk here of the highest virtue, who observed the Monastic Rules so faithfully that the people of the country suspected he must be an Arhat. When he was about to die the king came to visit him and, in accordance with the Buddhist custom, assembled all the monks. Then in their presence he asked this monk: "Have you attained to sainthood?"

At that the other told him the truth: "I am an Arhat."

After his death, the king had him cremated four or five *li* east of the monastery, in accordance with the funeral ceremony for Arhats decreed by the Monastic Rules. A fine, great pyre of wood was built, about thirty feet square and thirty feet high, with sandalwood, aloes and other aromatic wood at its top. Steps were made at the four sides, and the whole pyre was covered with snowy white woollen cloth of the best quality. Above the pyre would be the bier, similar to the hearse which is used in China, except that it had no dragon and fish designs. At the time of the cremation, the king and people, including all the believers of the four groups, assembled together. After offering flowers and incense, they followed the bier to the place of cremation. The king then made his personal offerings of flowers and incense. This done, the bier was placed on top of the pyre, great quantities of butter were poured over it, and it was set ablaze. As it burned, all present took off their upper garments to show their reverence, and from a distance cast these and their feather fans and parasols as additional fuel into the fire. After the cremation was over, they collected the remains over which to build a stupa. Fa Xian did not reach Simhala in time to see this Arhat in the flesh, but he witnessed his funeral ceremony.

The king, being an earnest believer in Buddhism, desired to build a new monastery for the monks. First of all he summoned a great assembly of monks and offered them a splendid feast. After offerings had been made he selected a pair of his best oxen, and adorned their horns with gold, silver and other precious objects. Then he himself ploughed the four sides of a plot of land with a fine golden plough, and ceded this land to the monks, with all the inhabitants, fields and houses on it. An iron titledeed was engraved and given them, to be handed down from generation to generation, for none would dare alter or annul it.

A Sermon Preached by an Indian Monk

While in this country Fa Xian heard an Indian monk, seated on his high seat, deliver the following sermon:

"Buddha's alms-bowl, which was first at Vaisali, is now at Gandhara. After several centuries (Fa Xian heard the monk mention a definite period of time but he has forgotten the exact number of years stated), it will go to the country of Western Sakas; after several more centuries it will go to the kingdom of Khotan; after several more centuries it will go to the kingdom of Kucha; after several more centuries it will go to China, where it will remain for several more centuries before going to Simhala;

and after several more centuries it will return to Central India. After having returned to Central India, it will ascend to the Tusita Heaven, where the Maitreya Bodhisattva on seeing it will exclaim:

"'The alms-bowl of Sakyamuni Buddha has arrived!'

"Then together with all the devas, he will offer flowers and incense to it for seven days. After the seven days it will return to Jambudvipa, where the king of the sea-dragons will carry it to his dragon-palace for safe keeping until Maitreya Bodhisattva is about to become a Buddha. The bowl will then be divided into four and returned to its original place on Mount Vinataka. * After Maitreya's accession to Buddha-hood, the four celestial kings will worship him in the same way as the former Buddhas. The thousand Buddhas of the *Bhadra-kalpa* all use this same alms-bowl. When this bowl vanishes, Buddhism will gradually disappear; and after it has disappeared, the life span of human beings will diminish to as little as five or ten years. By that time there will be no more rice or butter, and men will have grown so savage that even a piece of wood will serve as a weapon in their hands for injury and slaughter. Those who have done good deeds may escape to the mountains to avoid destruction, and come out again after all the evil-doers have killed themselves.

"'Man's life was once long,' they will say to each other. 'But as men were guilty of many sins and committed all manner of crimes, our life has been shortened to no more than ten years. Therefore let us all do good together and, with charity in our

---

* When Buddha first attained Buddha-hood, each of the four celestial kings presented him with an alms-bowl, and he combined the four into one. After Buddha's Nirvana this bowl became four again, and returned to Mount Vinataka.

hearts, cultivate virtue and righteousness.'

"Thus all will believe and conduct themselves with propriety, till by degrees their life span is lengthened to as many as 80,000 years. Then Maitreya Bodhisattva will be born into the world. When he begins to expound the Law he will first convert the followers and monks of the Law bequeathed by Sakyamuni Buddha, and those who make offerings to the Three Precious Gems, take refuge in Buddha, Dharma and Sangha and observe the Five or the Eight Precepts. The second and third groups will be those who are fit to be saved."

Fa Xian at that time wished to copy down this sermon.

"There is no written record," said the monk. "I deliver it orally only."

Fa Xian stayed in this country for two years, and obtained a copy of the *Rules of the Mahisasakas*. He also procured a copy of the *Dirghagama*, the *Samyuktagama*, and the *Sannipata*, all of which were unknown in China...

Translated by Yang Xianyi
and Gladys Yang

Carving a Dragon at the Core of Literature

THE author Liu Xie (c. AD 465-532 or c. AD 470-539), a literary critic under the Liang Dynasty, was born at Ju in Dongguan, now Juxian in Shandong, into an impoverished family. Determined to remain unmarried, he attached himself to the Buddhist monk Seng You, whom he assisted in the compilation of the sutras. After a succession of minor positions at court he came to the notice of the crown prince Xiao Tong, better known as Prince Zhao Ming, under whose auspices he produced the following monumental work. He eventually petitioned the emperor to be allowed to take Buddhist orders, which was granted, but he died soon after entering the clergy under the name of Hui Di.

His book, considered one of the highest authorities on Chinese literary criticism, not only expounds the techniques of writing but explores the history and development of Chinese literature from the *Book of Songs* down to his own day.

Carving a Dragon at the Core of Literature

On Fancy

The ancients said, "The body may be on the river or out at sea, while the heart lingers by the palace gate." This is what is meant by fancy. As for fancy in literature that goes much further. Thoughts shaped in silence can reach a thousand generations to come, while the eyes of the mind may see ten thousand *li* away. The writer with so subtle a fancy lets fall sounds like pearls or tinkling jade, while scenes unfold before his eyes like clouds shifting in the wind. The miracle of fancy lies in the human spirit's traffic with all creation. The spirit dwells in a man's breast and his will controls the lock; things come to his ears and meet his eyes, and language supplies the key. When this key serves, then nothing should remain hidden; when the lock is blocked, the spirit may disappear. So what is most needful in casting ideas into writing is the possession of a tranquil mind. A man should cleanse his heart, purify his spirit, amass knowledge to store up learning, use reason to increase his capabilities, study things carefully to improve his powers of observation, and train himself in the use of the right phrase. Then the mind, pre-eminent, can seek out rhythm to guide the pen and like a skilled craftsman give fitting form to ideas. So fancy is the prime requirement in writing, the root of any conception.

When we give rein to our fancy, innumerable paths open up a-head; we plot any course we please, inlay any invisible pattern.

Would we climb a mountain? Our spirit soars above it. Survey the ocean? Our ideas reach over the sea. Whatever talents we have seem to race with the wind and the clouds; we take up a pen, inspired beyond all telling, but the work when written may express only half of what was in our hearts. This is because an idea not yet formulated may easily seem striking but is hard to set down skilfully in so many words. Thoughts pass into ideas, ideas into language, sometimes corresponding so closely that no discrepancy exists, sometimes so loosely that a thousand *li* stretch between. An argument may be at hand while you seek it at the horizon; an idea may be hard by yet hid from your mind as if by mountains and rivers. So to improve his writing a man should train his mind and not count simply on cudgelling his brains. Once he knows the right way to express himself, no undue exertions are needed.

Men have different gifts: some are quick, others slow. In writing, some tasks are great and others small. Thus Sima Xiangru* gnawed through his brush, Yang Xiong dreamed a fearful dream after writing an essay, Huan Tan took such anxious thought that he fell ill, Wang Chong exhausted his strength through deep meditation, Zhang Heng spent ten years polishing his essay about the two capitals, and Zuo Si worked for a dozen years on his essay on the three imperial cities. True, some of

---

* Sima Xiangru (179-117 BC), famous Han-dynasty writer; Yang Xiong (53 BC-AD 18), famous Han-dynasty writer and scholar who compiled the *Local Dialects*, an important lexicon in ancient China; Huan Tan (24 BC-AD 56), Han-dynasty writer; Wang Chong (AD 27-91), famous Han-dynasty philosopher whose *Criterion of Argument* is an important philosophical work; Zhang Heng (AD 78-139), famous Han-dynasty writer; Zuo Si, famous poet of the third century AD; Prince of Huainan (179-122 BC), well-known Han-dynasty writer; and Mei Gao, Han-dynasty writer.

these were major works, but the writers were also slow thinkers. On the other hand, the Prince of Huainan finished his lament in one morning, Mei Gao composed essays on the spur of the moment at the imperial command, Cao Zhi* wrote as fast as if speaking, Wang Can** wielded his pen as if copying, Yuan Yu could dash off a letter in the saddle, Mi Heng*** could draft a report during a meal. These were shorter works, but these men were fast thinkers too. Men with quick minds readily grasp essentials and jump to rapid conclusions without much preliminary consideration, whereas men with slower minds tend to weigh all possibilities and reach a decision only after much deliberation, after first overcoming their doubts. A quick-witted man may accomplish a task in a flash, while the slower-witted takes time to achieve results. But though one way seems easy and the other hard, each depends on wide knowledge and intensive study. I have yet to hear of anything good achieved by a poor scholar working slowly, or by a dolt working fast. We face two difficulties, then, in marshalling our thoughts for writing: closed minds may result in poverty of speech, ideas that flow too freely may result in confusion. So wide knowledge is the best fare for those who lack substance, and a unifying thread of thought the best

---

* (AD 192-232) son of the famous statesman Cao Cao, an outstanding poet at the end of the Han Dynasty and a leader among contemporary poets.

** (AD 177-217) famous poet at the end of the Han Dynasty. He and Kong Rong (AD 153-208), Xu Gan (AD 170-217), Liu Zhen (AD? -217), Chen Lin, Yuan Yu (AD? -212) and Ying Yang were protégés of Cao Cao and his sons, and formed the most influential school of poetry at that time. They were known as the "seven writers of the Jinan period."

*** (AD 173-198) writer at the end of the Han Dynasty, who was killed because he offended Cao Cao.

remedy for those whose ideas are confused. It follows that the combination of wide knowledge with one unifying thread of thought will aid the writer in all he undertakes.

Again, feeling may be complex and forms of expression varied. A crude expression may bring out a subtle meaning, a commonplace incident may contain the germ of new ideas. Though hemp is no different from ordinary cotton, worked up by shuttle and loom it turns into some rich and rare material. But when it comes to the finest shades of meaning or intricacies beyond the power of language to express, the writer simply has to lay down his pen. A man must grasp the essence to be able to express all its subtlety, he must grasp all the changes to understand their laws. Yet Yi Yin* could not explain his use of the cauldron nor Lun Bian** his use of the axe, for the skill of each defied description.

Epitome:

    In images is fancy dressed
    To make its changes manifest;
    When objects strike upon our view
    The mind accords due sense thereto;
    Rhythm is born and melody,
    With all the laws of prosody;
    Well-marshalled thoughts, a well-stocked mind,
    And victory is close behind!

---

* Yi Yin was the adviser of King Tang who founded the Shang Dynasty (1562? - 1066? BC); Yi Yin was also supposed to be a good cook.

** According to legend, this man was a skilful carpenter.

On Sentiment and Structure

The *Book of Songs* * has six attributes, foremost of which is sentiment. This is the source of the power to move and change men, the manifestation of human aspirations. All expression of emotion and longing must start from sentiment, while the selection of apt words and phrases must start from the structure. Language requires structure just as a body requires a skeleton; emotion must embody sentiment just as the spirit is contained in the form. Words set out in stately fashion make up structure; a vigorous spirit makes for sentiment in writing. A plethora of fine phrases without nobility of sentiment and structure is like colour drained of its brightness or a voice devoid of strength. When arranging ideas for writing we must store up ample spirit and to spare, for strength and vigour within will bring forth fresh splendour. Literature depends on spirit just as swift birds depend on their wings to fly.

One who labours over the structure will gain a fine command of language; one with deep sentiment will express emotion vividly. When language is so closely knit that no change can be made and the rhythm is controlled yet not sluggish, this is due to sentiment and structure. Poverty of thought couched in rich language, a profusion of words without a central idea, indicates the absence of structure just as a weak flow of ideas and spiritless writing indicate the absence of sentiment. When Pan Xu** drafted the im-

---

* China's earliest anthology of poetry.
** A writer at the end of the Han Dynasty.

perial edict appointing Cao Cao the Duke of Wei, he took the style of old documents as his model and so noble was his structure that all other men of talent laid down their pens. When Sima Xiangru wrote about immortals, his spirit soared to the clouds and so exalted was his sentiment that he became the father of descriptive poetry. Once we have grasped these essentials we can regulate our writing with them, while if we depart from them no amount of embellishments will serve any purpose.

Thus Emperor Wen of Wei* said, "In writing, the spirit is paramount. There are nobler and baser spirits in literature. Neither is the result of effort, however hard." Of Kong Rong he said, "His spirit is noble and fine." Of Xu Gan, "Sometimes he is slow like the men of Qi." Of Liu Zhen, "He has vigour." Liu Zhen also said, "Kong Rong is certainly outstanding with his truly remarkable spirit and inimitable style." All these comments show the stress laid on the spirit of a writing. The pheasant, for all its variegated plumage, is too plump and heavy to fly more than a hundred paces; while drab though the eagle's colours, thanks to its strong bones and fiery spirit, it soars up to the sky. The same is true of talent in literature. Sentiment and structure without colour are like vultures gathering in the world of learning, while colour without sentiment and structure is like pheasants scurrying into the field of letters. Only the clear-voiced phoenix has both splendid plumage and the power to soar high in the realm of writing.

By casting writing in classical moulds, studying the methods of philosophers and historians, delving into changes in style, and

---

* Cao Pi, poet, eldest son of Cao Cao.

understanding the forms of literature we can give birth to new ideas and fashion striking images. Once the various forms of literature are clear, the ideas will be fresh but not confused. Once changes in styles are understood, the language will be striking but not bizarre. If before a man succeeds in combining structure and embellishments or perfecting his language to convey sentiment, he tries to bypass the old rules and hasten on to new forms, he may hit upon ingenious ideas but the likelihood of failure will be even greater. As for stringing startling phrases together, this may in time become a pernicious habit. The *Zhou Documents**
says: "In language aptness ranks above novelty." This was a warning against the misuse of language. There are many ways of writing, however, and every writer has his own preference. When those who understand may not teach and those learning may not find the right masters, writers tend to seek glitter and show, flouting the rules and forgetting the right path. If men would firmly adopt the proper models to make their writing clear and vigorous, then it would possess noble sentiment, firm structure and a splendid form. When these points are grasped, the goal is not far to seek.

Epitome:

Spirit and feeling side by side,
Language and form must be allied;
Let lucid strength your lines pervade
To shine like pendants of bright jade;

---

* Ancient historical records of the Zhou Dynasty, part of the *Book of Documents* which according to tradition was compiled by Confucius.

Fine sentiment should be combined
With structure vigorous and refined;
Then wit as keen as sharpest blade
Will shine with splendour of brocade.

On Feeling and Art

The works of sages and worthies are generally known as fine writing, and what is this if not "art"? Just as ripples form in water which is fluid and flowers grow from wood which is solid, so art depends on substance. Just as tigers and leopards have markings to distinguish them from dogs and sheep, while rhinoceroshide armour is varnished red, so substance has to be adorned by art. When it comes to setting forth human nature, delineating objects, committing ideas to writing and spinning language on paper, art is needed for splendour. So there are three elements in writing: one is form, or the Five Colours; another is sound, or the Five Notes of music; the third is feeling or the Five Emotions. The Five Colours blend to make rich designs, the Five Notes combine to make enchanting music, the Five Emotions set forth in writing move men's hearts. This is the order of nature.

Since the *Book of Filial Piety** enjoins men not to use ornate language while mourning, it appears that the customary speech of a gentleman was not plain and unadorned. Lao Zi,** who abhorred hypocrisy, said that fair speech could not be trusted; yet even he did not repudiate beauty, for his book in five thousand

---

* One of the Confucian canons.

** Outstanding ancient philosopher and founder of the Taoist school, who wrote *The Way and Its Power*.

words is superbly written. Zhuang Zi, * speaking of meticulous definitions, had in mind the artifice of rhetoric. And Han Fei, ** urging the use of conceits in argument, was referring to literary embellishment. Arguments adorned with embellishments and artifice in rhetoric mark writing of the highest quality.

A study of the *Book of Filial Piety* and *The Way and Its Power* shows that both art and substance depend on feeling. A careful perusal of Zhuang Zi and Han Fei reveals that over-ornateness may lead to licence. One who can distinguish the waters of confluent streams, who reins in his steed at the crossroad to choose the right way, can also check literary embellishment. Just as paint and powder may improve the appearance but beauty comes from good features, so literary adornment may improve language but splendour springs from feeling. Thus feeling is the warp of writing and language the woof of reason, only when the warp is in place can the woof be woven, and only when reason is firm can language flow freely. This is the root of writing.

The poets of old used art to vent their feelings, while later writers of descriptive poems counterfeited feeling for the sake of art. Why do I say this? Because the men who made the old folksongs sang to vent the grief and anger in their hearts and satirize those above. This is what is meant by writing to vent feeling. But Han-dynasty poets, who had no sorrow in their hearts but hunted for hyperboles to dazzle the world and win a name for themselves, were counterfeiting feeling for art. Those who wrote to vent feeling were succinct and truthful; those who

---

* (369-? BC) outstanding ancient philosopher of the Taoist school.
** (? -233 BC) outstanding ancient philosopher.

wrote for the sake of art were magniloquent and wearisome. Poets since that time have chosen magniloquence and discarded truth, turning their backs on the ancient songs and odes to imitate the Han descriptive poems, so that writing expressing true feeling grows daily rarer while meretricious verses are all the fashion. Thus some who hanker after official honours pay lip service to the pleasures of country life, while others whose hearts are set on power affect a desire to escape from the world of men. There is no truth in them, they have left the Way.

Peach and plum have no voice, yet because they bear fruit paths are trodden out to them. Orchids planted by a rough fellow have no fragrance, because he himself lacks feeling. If even trees and plants must have feeling and substance, how much more so must literature. The prime task of literature is to express man's will! When words run counter to true feeling, art is worthless!

Phrases are linked and colour interwoven to light up some idea, but when colour runs riot and language becomes far-fetched, the meaning is obscured. Using cassia as bait and a kingfisher's feather as fly will never catch a fish — this is what is meant by language veiled by splendour. Thus a hempen garment should be worn outside silk to avoid ostentation, and the oracle counted simplicity auspicious because it is good to return to nature. If men can take reason as their guide and keep emotion within proper bounds, once emotion is under control music can be made; once reason is in command embellishments can be adopted; for then neither will art ruin substance nor profusion of images blur the central theme, but true reds and blues will shine out while mawkish pinks and purples are set aside. Language like this, fashioned with skill, is worthy of the name of fine writing.

Epitome:
Through art words travel wide:
This maxim is well-tried.
Thoughts shaped within the heart
Their radiance will impart;
Soon solled the rare brocade,
Hibiscus sweet must fade;
Empty magniloquence
Must jar upon the sense.

On Hyperbole

Above form is the Way, below it are physical objects. The world of the spirit is so hard to grasp that not even the subtlest language can trace it to the end; but physical objects are easy to describe and their true form can be expressed in forceful phrases. It is not that some writers have more talent than others, but simply that one is easier to describe. So all things in heaven or on earth find expression in sound and appearance, and to clothe them in language frequent use is made of hyperbole. Even classical works like the *Book of Songs* and the *Book of Documents*, which serve as models to instruct men, inevitably cover such a wide range that recourse is often had to exaggeration. Thus height becomes "heaven-piercing peaks", narrowness "a river too small to hold a barge", a large family "millions of offspring", few inhabitants "not a soul left alive", a flood "waters surging to the sky", a defeat "the very pestles were floating in blood". This high-flown language does no violence, however, to the sense. But not even poets can make an owl's hoot melodious or transform bitter herbs into sweet. It was indeed their passion to praise that made them employ this artifice and great sages recorded these examples for future writers. Thus Mencius[*] said, "When studying the songs, do not let their music blind you to the words, nor the words blind you to the meaning."

With Song Yu and Jing Chai,[**] hyperbole came into fashion. Sima Xiangru followed in their steps and went to extremes. In his descriptions of the imperial forest, shooting stars and curved rainbows alight on the pavilions, while game is so plentiful that griffins and phoenixes are caught. Yang Xiong's writing of the Ganquan Palace came under his influence and described rare plants as trees of jade, buildings as so high that even spirits must tumble down from them. As for some accounts of the east and west capitals, their reports of strange fish and sea monsters pass all bounds of credibility yet fall short of the most splendid imagery. Again, Yang Xiong's description of an imperial hunt has the river goddess whipped to appease Qu Yuan, while Zhang Heng has the God of Water besieged in the Northern Wilderness. Now the Goddess of the River Luo is no water demon, nor is the God of Water a mountain ogre. This is a slipshod use of fantastic allusions. The intention here was to heighten the effect, but the similes are too far-fetched. As for the appearance of mountains and seas or the aspect of courts and palaces, these tower in beauty or dazzle by their splendour, so magnificent they must surely

---

[*] (372-289 BC) well-known philosopher of the Confucian school.

[**] Poets of the Kingdom of Chu of the third to second century BC.

burst into flame, so steep they must surely topple down. All these depend upon exaggeration and owe their novelty to artifice. So later writers prize hyperbole. They spread their wings to soar high or leap and bound, scorning to hobble along. Do they speak of splendour? Spring flowers cannot match its brightness. Of decay? A wintry chasm is less desolate. Of joy? Words and laughter intermingle. Of sadness? Voices blend with sobs. They undoubtedly know how to release pent-up feelings, put boredom to flight, make the blind see and rouse the deaf.

However, when rhetoric oversteps the mark, discourse becomes confused; when exaggeration outstrips reason, name and reality are at variance. If we can absorb the general principles of the *Book of Songs* and *Book of Documents*, pruning the excesses of Yang Xiong and Sima Xiangru so as to have restraint in exaggeration and embellishment without falsification, the result will be admirable.

Epitome:

Employ hyperbole aright,
A writer has no constant law;
The spirit should not lag in flight,
Like giant roc let language soar!
For pearls men search the ocean bed,
Of jade the mountains have good store;
Let writing brim, not overflow,
Extravagant yet free from flaw.

On Discrimination

Discrimination is rare. Indeed it is hard to appreciate art, hard to find a true connoisseur — there may be only one such in a thousand years! Most critics since early times have held their own generation cheap and admired the ancients. This is known as spurning those things close at hand every day and longing for the music heard in the distance. When Han Fei's writings first appeared and Sima Xiangru first completed his poem, the Emperor of Qin and the Emperor Wu of Han wished these men were contemporaries; but once they discovered these writers were still alive, Han Fei was thrown into gaol and Sima Xiangru treated with contempt. Is this not a clear indication that men hold contemporary writing cheap?

There was little to choose between Ban Gu* and Fu Yi** as writers, yet Ban Gu sneered at Fu Yi, saying, "He cannot lay down his pen when he starts writing." Again Cao Zhi, speaking of talent, laughed at Chen Lin; but when asked to touch up Ding Yi's*** writing Cao Zhi thought this an excellent scheme, while he compared his detractor Liu Xiu to Tian Ba.**** All this reveals his bias. So it was not for nothing that Emperor Wen of Wei remarked that scholars despise each other.

---

* (AD 32-92) famous Han-dynasty historian.

** (AD? -89) Han-dynasty poet.

*** A writer at the end of the Han Dynasty. He asked Cao Zhi to polish his writing and said, "I know myself the merits and defects of my writing. No one in future generations will know who edited my works."

**** Liu Xiu, a writer at the end of the Han Dynasty. He had little talent but liked to criticize people; Tian Ba, an orator in the third century BC.

Then there was that babbler Lou Hu* who thought he could hold forth on literature and made Huan Tan and others laugh by maintaining that Sima Qian consulted Dongfang Shuo.** If a mere playboy like Lou Hu made a fool of himself by irresponsible talk, scholars should watch their tongues much more carefully. So there are men of perception, like the two emperors, who value the ancients and despise the moderns; there are men of outstanding talent, like Ban Gu and Cao Zhi, who think highly of themselves and look down on others; and there are men lacking any knowledge of literature, like Lou Hu, who believe in what is false and are blind to the truth. No wonder, then, if some lament that writing is used as waste paper to cover a pot of sauce!

The unicorn and phoenix are utterly different from the stag and pheasant; pearls and jade are quite unlike pebbles and stones. Sunlight illumines them clearly for men's eyes to take in their forms, yet a subject of Lu took a unicorn for a stag, a man of Chu took a pheasant for a phoenix, a native of Wei took jade for a curious stone, a citizen of Song took a pebble for a precious pearl. If they made such mistakes over forms like these which are easy to distinguish, of course it is difficult to distinguish between styles of writing which are hard to grasp.

Writing takes many forms, being compounded of substance and of art. Most men have certain prejudices which prevent them from seeing things in the round. The liberal may applaud a heroic strain, the thoughtful may respond to subtleties, the superfi-

---

* A Han-dynasty orator.

** (154-93 BC) a Han-dynasty jester.

cially clever may delight in show, those with a taste for the bizarre may wonder at strange tales. When the writing suits them they exclaim with pleasure, but when it is not to their taste they reject it. Each sees the infinite variety of literature from his own particular viewpoint. This is what is meant by the saying: "A man facing east cannot see the western wall."

After playing a thousand tunes a man understands music; after examining a thousand swords he understands weapons. So to gain an idea of literature as a whole we must first read widely. A view of high mountains shows the shape of hills; a dip in the ocean illustrates the shallowness of a ditch. Only a man with no prejudices great or small, no personal likes or dislikes, can weigh things up fairly and see writing as clearly as in a mirror. To examine the merits of any work of literature we must establish six criteria and consider: first, the style adopted; secondly, the language used; thirdly, the development from past traditions; fourthly, the methods of expression; fifthly, the arguments and allusions; and sixthly, the musical rhythm. After this is done, we can determine whether a work is good or bad.

The writer, aroused by feeling, is moved to expression; the reader poring over his writing enters into his feeling. If we seek the source by following the stream, we shall find it even if it lies concealed. We cannot meet the men of old face to face, but by reading their works we can see into their hearts. No writing is too deep to penetrate, the sole danger is too shallow an understanding. If a man thinking of mountains and rivers can express his feeling on the lyre, how can ideas embodied by the pen escape us? The mind grasps an idea just as the eyes perceive objects. Good eyes can distinguish between all manner of objects, and an intelligent mind can penetrate any idea. But vulgar critics may be confused, discarding what is profound to seek out what is shallow. This is why Zhuang Zi laughed at those who admired the song *Plucking the Willow*, * and Song Yu lamented that men could not appreciate music like *White Snow*. ** Qu Yuan once said, "Art and nature lay within me, but the crowd did not see my rare splendour." Only a true connoisseur can discern what is finest. Yang Xiong affirmed that he loved profound and brilliant writing, proving that he too was dissatisfied with mere show. A man of deep understanding and keen observation will have the same pleasure in his mind as a crowd of revellers on the terrace in spring or travellers stopping for good music and food. Just as the orchid, king of fragrant flowers, becomes more fragrant when worn; so books, which are sovereign flowers too, reveal their beauty when studied and analysed. Let men of discrimination ponder this!

Epitome:
  Great bells there are of weight untold,
  Their tones set true by men of old;
  And crates of books are heaped up high
  Awaiting a discerning eye;
  A wanton tune leads men astray,

---

* A popular air.
** A tune enjoyed by the élite.

Best close your ears and walk away.
All those who hold these rules in sight
Will never stray from what is right.

Translated by Yang Xianyi
and Gladys Yang

图书在版编目（CIP）数据

汉魏六朝诗文选/(晋)陶渊明等著;杨宪益,戴乃迭译.-北京:外文出版社,2003.11
（熊猫丛书）
ISBN 7-119-03356-5

Ⅰ.汉... Ⅱ.①陶...②杨...③戴... Ⅲ.英语−语言读物,古典文学
Ⅳ.H319.4:Ⅰ

中国版本图书馆 CIP 数据核字(2003)第 055135 号

外文出版社网址：
　http://www.flp.com.cn
外文出版社电子信箱：
　info@flp.com.cn
　sales@flp.com.cn

熊猫丛书

汉魏六朝诗文选

作　　者　陶渊明等
译　　者　杨宪益　戴乃迭等
责任编辑　陈海燕　李　芳
封面设计　唐少文
印刷监制　张国祥
出版发行　外文出版社
社　　址　北京市百万庄大街 24 号　　邮政编码　100037
电　　话　（010）68320579（总编室）
　　　　　（010）68329514/68327211（推广发行部）
印　　刷　北京中印联印务有限公司
经　　销　新华书店/外文书店
开　　本　大 32 开
印　　数　2001—5000 册　　印　　张　7.125
版　　次　2006 年第 1 版第 2 次印刷
装　　别　平
书　　号　ISBN 7-119-03356-5
　　　　　10−E−3567P
定　　价　21.00 元